FROM THE SUN'S  TO THE ELECTRONS OF THE ATOM . . .

. . . the spectroscope has served science in discovering the nature of matter and the composition of the universe. Based on a principle three centuries old, this invaluable instrument is serving physicists, chemists, astronomers, and many other scientists in their ever-widening exploration of the world around us.

In clear, concise language, the author traces the history of spectroscopy, explains the functioning of the spectroscope, and describes its manifold uses in the scientific disciplines of today and tomorrow. X-ray spectroscopy and the realm of the invisible spectrum . . . Humason's extraordinary red-shift spectrum from galaxies as distant as 700 million light-years . . . the energy "jumps" within atomic nuclei . . . these are but a few of the fascinating phenomena which Dr. Reid clarifies in terms readily understandable by laymen as well as science students. Aiding the text throughout are numerous diagrams and drawings by Laszlo Acs, and a wealth of photographs.

Other SIGNET SCIENCE Books
of Related Interest

The
Spectroscope

R. W. REID

With drawings by Laszlo Acs

A SIGNET SCIENCE LIBRARY BOOK

Published by The New American Library,
New York and Toronto

Published as a SIGNET SCIENCE LIBRARY BOOK
by arrangement with Weidenfeld & Nicolson, Ltd.,
who have authorized this softcover edition.

FIRST PRINTING, JULY, 1966

Acknowledgments
The author is indebted to The Royal Astronomical Society, the Ronan Picture Library, Messrs Hilger and Watts Limited and the General Electric Hirst Research Centre for permission to reproduce photographs in this book.

SIGNET SCIENCE LIBRARY BOOKS are published
in the United States by The New American Library, Inc.,
1301 Avenue of the Americas, New York, New York 10019,
in Canada by The New American Library of Canada Limited,
295 King Street East, Toronto 2, Ontario

PRINTED IN THE UNITED STATES OF AMERICA

Contents

The
Spectroscope

1

Newton's Experiment

Man is an inquisitive animal. For hours, years and even lifetimes he struggles to solve Nature's mysteries, not necessarily because he expects to make himself more rich, or more famous, but because he cannot let the challenge to discover go by unheeded: he must find out. The challenge, however, is formidable. It is as though Nature is a mastermind which sets one problem after another; each problem Man solves makes him more fitted to tackle something more difficult and exacting.

The scope of Nature is breathtaking. If we are to begin to understand her mysteries we must learn to explain the smallest and the largest, the nearest and the farthest. What does this mean in terms of the world around us? How small is the smallest and how far is the farthest? An atom is one of the smallest particles of matter. There are as many atoms in a single grain of sand as there are grains of sand necessary to fill a hundred St. Paul's Cathedrals. An atom is so small that not only can we not see it, we can scarcely imagine it. And just as Nature's most minute taxes our imagination so does Nature's most immense. Some of the most faint and distant stars which can be seen are more than ten thousand million million million miles away from us: and if this does not stagger our imagination, we can rest assured that there are still more distant stars which we cannot see.

The task of Science is to understand this huge expanse of Nature and scientists have set about building instruments to help their understanding. During this century an instrument has been perfected which can give us information about not only the tiny atom, but also about the even more minute particles which go to make up an atom. The instrument tells us what these particles are, how they move, and how they behave. It is a fantastic probe into the hidden mysteries of Nature. But more surprising still is that *the same instrument* can be used to tell us the secrets of the most distant of the stars; it tells us what the stars are made of, how they are moving, and at what speed. The atom is so minute that we cannot imagine its size: a faint star is at such a distance that we could only hope to reach it by travelling in space for millions of years—and yet one instrument gives us enough information to give a remarkably detailed description of both these extremes of Nature. This instrument is called *the spectroscope*, and how it is used by atomic physicists and astronomers is only part of its story; let us see how it came into being.

If any man were allowed to make a claim to be the father of the spectroscope then that man would be Sir Isaac Newton. Newton was born on Christmas Day, 1642, and over the fireplace in the room in which he was born is a stone tablet on which is carved the couplet of the poet Alexander Pope:

> Nature and Nature's Laws lay hid in night;
> God said, Let Newton be! And all was light.

It is in this way that Pope expresses the great achievements in the world of science of Newton. At school, and as an undergraduate at Cambridge it seems that, although he was clever, he was not outstandingly so. The groundwork for his preparation for Cambridge would undoubtedly have been in Greek and Latin along with a little Hebrew, and Biblical history and grammar for good measure. There is little doubt that the only scientific subject of his schooldays was mathematics, and that limited to arithmetic and geometry. It is therefore surprising that Newton should have interested himself with experiments in what we would now call physics. One branch of this subject which particularly attracted his attention was the study of the behaviour of light. It is said that as a boy, on winter nights he would frighten the local villagers by making lanterns from paper and a candle, and flying them from the tails of kites.

In 1665 the Great Plague was raging throughout Europe and in London alone there were more than 30,000 deaths from this terrible disease. Because of the fear of an outbreak in Cambridge the University was closed and Newton returned to live for two years in his native village of Woolsthorpe in Lincolnshire. In the history of science there are no parallels to the achievements of Newton, a young man in his early twenties, during these two years. Working in his own home he made three miraculous contributions to science, any one of which would have given him eternal fame. First, he invented the mathematical calculus which helped to revolutionise the science of mathematics; secondly, he discovered the law of gravitation by means of which he was able to explain the motions of the planets, and lastly, he began the science of optics. It is this last achievement with which we shall be concerned in this book, for from these studies of the behaviour of light sprang the knowledge of Newton's followers which enabled them to build, among many other instruments, *the spectroscope*.

In those days the telescope was as new and exciting as are atomic physics, radar or television today and it is not at all surprising that the young Newton should build himself a telescope with which to look at the stars. During his observations Newton became rather disappointed with some of the images he saw through high-powered telescopes, believing them to be capable of far better results than he was getting. For one thing the images of the objects which he observed were not at all clear or sharp, and furthermore the edges of the images were always faint, and coloured with the colours of the rainbow. He attributed these colours to some fault of the telescope lenses and decided to experiment in order to find their cause.

The two main sources of light which Newton had at his disposal were the candle and the Sun. These were the sources Newton used when he set out to investigate the reason for the coloured edges of images produced by high-powered telescopes. In the seventeenth century colour was a strange phenomenon which men of science had great difficulty in explaining. Indeed some of their explanations are most meaningless and confusing. For example, Kepler wrote: "Colour is potential light buried in pellucid matter", whatever that may mean. Some thought that colour was the result of a reaction between a substance and white light. It was thought that an apple was red because of a chemical reaction between a substance in the skin of the apple and the light falling on it. Others thought that colours were the result of a mixture of the two quantities, light and dark. Adopting this theory, an Italian philosopher who was also an archbishop, Antonius de Dominus, wrote in 1611, "If some darkness be mingled with the light, which yet permits it a passage and is not completely absorbed, there then occur the intermediate colours. On that account our fire appears reddish because it is mixed with smoke which darkens it." De Dominus was as far from the answer as Kepler.

This was the state of knowledge when Newton gathered together the equipment necessary to begin his investigations on colour. In a record of his accounts for 1665 we are told that at Stourbridge Fair he bought a glass *prism*. This, as we shall see, was to be the birth of the *spectroscope*.

His early experiments were extremely simple ones and can be repeated with the minimum of equipment. Newton took a strip of white paper and painted the left half blue and the right half red; he then took his prism and looked at the strip of paper as shown in Figure 1-1 (a) and saw that the blue left-hand half appeared to be above the red half (Figure 1-1 (b)).

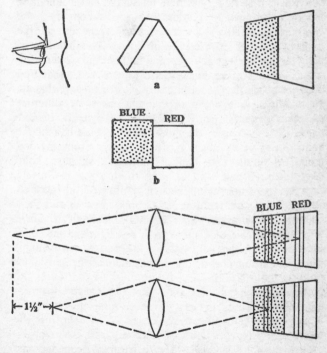

Fig. 1-1 and Fig. 1-2. Newton's experiments

Newton now wound some black silk thread around each half of his blue and red paper strip and illuminated it as best he could with candle light. Using a convex lens he focused the black threads, which crossed the red strip, as sharply as possible on a sheet of white paper and noticed that the black lines on the blue strip were blurred and not in focus. In order to focus the thread on the blue strip he had to move the white screen one and a half inches closer to the lens (Figure 1-2), when the lines on the red strip now became blurred.

The result of these experiments was that Newton was able to draw some most important conclusions. He knew that light, when it passes from air to glass, or air to liquids, or liquids to glass, is bent, and the amount of bending (or *refraction*) depends on the type of glass or on the type of liquid. This bending of light is easily seen by dipping a stick in water: the stick appears to be bent at the join of the water and the air above it (see Plate I). Newton's experiments had shown that coloured light is bent by different amounts depending on the colour. Thus in his experiment with the prism, the light from the blue half of the paper strip is *refracted* more than that from the red half and so the blue half of the paper appears to be above the red half.

The experiment with the lens confirmed this conclusion; a lens acts like a series of small prisms and so is able to focus light which is shone through it. Since blue light is refracted more than red light the image of the thread on the blue half of the paper was brought to a focus one and a half inches nearer the lens than that on the red half.

Incidentally, at this point Newton realised that using simple lenses in telescopes of high power would always give blurred and coloured images and so he perfected a type of telescope which used a mirror instead of an object glass (the *reflecting telescope*) and so avoided the tiresome colour effects of refraction. In this way he managed to obtain images which were not spoiled by having indistinct and coloured edges.

We know that Newton's next experiment was carried out in his room at Trinity College, Cambridge, and for it he needed a stronger light source than a candle. The only strong source of light available in those days was the Sun itself, and so Newton cut a hole about one third of an inch in diameter in the window blind and directed the Sun's rays at his prism (Figure 1-3). Eighteen feet from the prism Newton

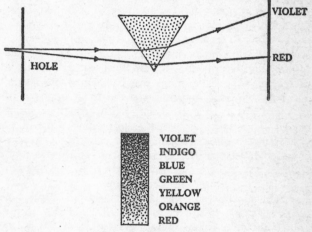

Fig. 1-3. The Spectrum

placed a white screen, calculating that he should see a simple image of the hole 2½ inches in diameter. However, to his great surprise, he saw no such thing. Instead of the image of a circular hole being projected on to the screen there was a vertical strip of light 2½ inches wide and 10 inches long. Stranger still was that the strip was coloured over its whole length in the same way that the rainbow is coloured: that is, red, orange, yellow, green, blue, indigo and violet. This band of colours is called a *spectrum*, and Newton's experiment in his college room was the first step towards the *spectroscope*. The significance of his experiment was immediately obvious to Newton and he realised that *white light is a mixture of rays of different colours* and that *these colours are refracted by different amounts by a glass prism*. Red light is refracted least, and violet light is refracted most, as his earlier experiments showed, whilst intermediate colours of the spectrum are refracted by amounts between these two extremes.

In any age, whenever a scientific theory as important as that of Newton is put forward there are always opponents ready to question, ridicule and deny the results. This is not an unhealthy sign; it merely means that a scientist must be sufficiently clever to outwit his opponents by re-testing and verifying his results. Such verifications were well within Newton's power, and the experiment which clinched his results and silenced his opponents was the exact opposite of the experiment he carried out in his room at Cambridge. That is to say, instead of taking white light and splitting it into its constituent colours, he took a coloured spectrum and recombined the colours to form white light. He formed his spectrum in the normal manner by passing sunlight through a prism (A in Figure 1-4); he then passed the spectrum through a convex lens on to a second prism, B, and saw to his delight that the beam of light coming from the prism was white sunlight, without any sign of the spectral colours which came from A. Newton had rebuilt white light from its component colours.

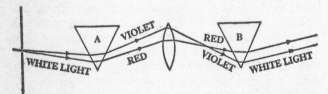

Fig. 1-4. Newton's experiment recombining spectral light to form white light

It was not until 1671, six or seven years after his first series of experiments, that Newton sent his "New Theory of Light and Colour" to the Royal Society of

London. The learned gentlemen of the Society were most impressed and "ordered that the author be solemnly thanked, in the name of the Society, for this very ingenious discourse . . . and that the Bishop of Salisbury, Mr. Boyle and Mr. Hook, be desired to peruse and consider it." Peruse and consider they did, and soon Newton's genius was acknowledged. His work had marked the beginning of a new era in science.

2

The Rainbow

Newton, of course, was not the first man to see a spectrum. Every day, somewhere in the world, Nature is producing her own spectrum—the rainbow, and it is worth while pausing in the story of the spectroscope to see what can be learned from this wonderful sight. The explanation of the rainbow must at first have taxed man's imagination as much as the explanation of the movements of the planets and the stars. But although the beauty of the rainbow impressed the primitive scientist it can never have overawed him as did the majesty of the stars or the glory of the Sun. He was so sure of the power of these heavenly bodies that he used to worship them and held them responsible for the trials and tribulations of daily life. In England there are still remains of stone circles which were used at one time or another as temples by Sun worshippers; Stonehenge is perhaps the most famous of these.

Today there are still considerable numbers of people who firmly believe that the stars are responsible for our individual destinies. But the rainbow, pretty as it is, has never been honoured by being held to be capable of such wonderful powers. The reason for this is probably quite a simple one: man found that he could make his own rainbow. Even the earliest observer of the rainbow cannot fail to have noticed that this arc of colours always occurred when strong sunlight shone on to falling rain, and that he saw the effect only when he was *between* the sun and the rain. And the same thing happened if he made his own rain as spray from fountains or waterfalls; provided he stood between the sun and the spray, a rainbow, or part of a rainbow, would often occur. You can try this for yourself by suitably positioning a garden hose to give a fine water spray and by standing between the Sun and the spray. With a little luck and experimenting you can have your own rainbow!

The greatest mystery about the rainbow was that it was not possible for the observer to stand directly underneath it or actually in the colours: he had to be between it and the sun. So grew up the story that at the unattainable end of this bow of many colours were some very rare finds—a pot of gold is the favourite rarity, though Venezuelan Indians have it that there are serpents' heads there. The end of the rainbow has yet to be found, and so has the pot of gold.

We know that the Greek and Roman philosophers attempted unsuccessfully to explain the origin of the rainbow; in particular they tried to explain the fact that in some bows violet was the uppermost colour of the arc followed by indigo, blue, green, yellow, orange, whilst finally red was the colour nearest the earth; in other cases red was the topmost colour and violet the lowest, the intermediate colours occurring in the reverse order. Sometimes both types of rainbow could be seen together in the sky and these became known as *primary* and *secondary* rainbows.

It was not until the late sixteenth century that an explanation which was almost correct was produced. This was due to Archbishop de Dominus, whose theory of colours we have already mentioned. It was he who suggested that light was probably reflected *inside* the raindrop. It was a well known fact that light shining through water could be reflected at the surface of the air back through the water, in the same way that sunlight shining through the air can be reflected from the surface of the water back through the air. Using de Dominus' explanation of reflection inside the drop together with Newton's theory of the composition of light we are now in a position to explain just how these two rainbows are formed.

Figure 2-1 (b) shows sunlight entering a raindrop at D where the ray is refracted. However, in this case the light suffers not one but two reflections, at E and F, before leaving the drop at G. If the paths of the red and violet light are followed it is seen that because of the additional reflection inside the drop, red becomes the uppermost colour and the order of the colours of the rainbow is inverted.

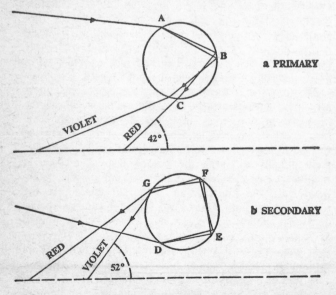

Fig. 2-1. How raindrops refract light to form primary and secondary rainbows

Because of the precise conditions under which the sunlight is reflected in a drop of liquid, in this case a raindrop, the spectrum of colours is only seen by an observer when it emerges at certain angles. If we imagine the observer and a point on earth under the centre of the rainbow's arc to be joined by a line, then the primary rainbow will always make an angle of approximately 42° with this line. In the case of the secondary rainbow the angle is approximately 52° and so the secondary must always be expected to appear outside the primary rainbow. The secondary is usually fainter and broader than the primary.

A visitor to Victoria Falls in Rhodesia can spend fascinating moments watching the arcs of both primary and secondary rainbows in the late afternoons. The spray from these huge falls rains down over a wide area of the surrounding forest. At the right time of day a walk along the edge of the chasm down which the Zambesi tumbles, will reveal to the visitor, in this gorge below his own level, part of a cup-shaped (rather than a dome-shaped) rainbow. Rainbows can also be formed by reflection of sunlight from the surface of a lake or any other water surface, and when this happens the rainbow is more than a semicircle and its centre is above the horizon; at the same time it is possible to see the rainbow formed in the normal way by direct rays from the sun.

There is no reason why the moon should not produce its own rainbow on wet evenings, and indeed there are many people who have been lucky enough to see this rare sight.

These, and many other examples, are the ways in which Nature makes her spectrum, and Newton was of course imitating Nature when he used a prism to split light into its constituent colours. Newton's important experiment showing how the colours of the spectrum recombine to form white light is by no means unknown in Nature. The appearance of a rainbow— the width of the coloured bands and their brightness

—depends on the size of the raindrops. If raindrops are as small as about 0.1 mm. in diameter the bands become very narrow and the colours are super-imposed on top of each other. When this happens the spectral colours are recombined and the rainbow looks almost white and is very faint. This type of bow is known as Ulloa's Ring or a fogbow.

3

The First
Spectroscope

William Wollaston was a doctor who practised in Huntingdon and Bury St. Edmunds. He was quite a successful physician and in 1797 he moved to London where he started a medical practice in the Strand. We are told that he was a quiet and reserved man who enjoyed spending his leisure hours carrying out scientific experiments. In 1800 he was left a small sum of money and this is possibly the reason why he decided to abandon the medical profession to devote the whole of his time to scientific research. However, another reason why it is suggested that he could no longer continue as a doctor was because of his over-anxiety on behalf of his patients. On one occasion a question about a patient caused him to burst into tears. Whatever the reason, in 1801 he took a house at 14, Buckingham Street, Fitzroy Square and at the back set up a laboratory. Within five years he discovered an industrial process concerned with the metal platinum which brought him in a fortune of £30,000, and he soon became one of Europe's foremost scientists.

Quite shortly after moving into Buckingham Street, Wollaston took up the investigation of the spectrum using a prism and lenses, as Newton had done over a hundred years earlier. But Wollaston saw that in order to obtain a clearer spectrum, it was necessary to restrict the light being examined, not by a hole, as did Newton, but by a very narrow slit. This simple invention was to be of great significance in the history of modern science. Wollaston arranged his optical system as shown in Figure 3-1, and this combination of prism and slit is what we today call the *spectroscope*. The principle of the arrangement of lenses, slit and prism is the same in even the most modern of spectroscopes.

The spectroscope can be used to investigate any source of light; Wollaston was particularly interested in the Sun, but a flame, a lamp, or even the stars can be examined equally well. Light from the source is focused on to the slit by a lens called a *condensing* lens. Before passing through the prism the light must be made parallel; this is done by a *collimating* lens. The prism splits the light into the colours of the spectrum and these are focused on to a screen by the *object* lens. Alternatively it is possible to look directly at the spectrum by replacing the screen by another lens, the eye-piece.

The spectra which Newton produced were always unclear, and it was difficult to see which colours were present in each particular spectrum. The reason for

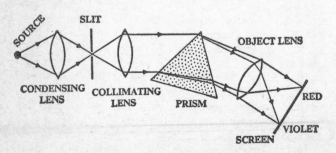

Fig. 3-1. Wollaston's optical arrangements

this was that Newton was producing what was in effect a series of different coloured images of his pinhole, each of which overlapped the next, so that the result was never a very clear picture. With Wollaston's narrow slit method, however, there is only a small amount of overlapping of neighbouring images of the slit, and what we see is a clear and well-defined spectrum. The narrower the slit, then the better in appearance is the spectrum, though of course it is more difficult to see since closing the slit reduces the amount of light allowed into the spectroscope.

Like Newton, Wollaston had few sources of light available to focus on the slit of his spectroscope and so he would often use the Sun as a convenient source. One day he pointed his spectroscope at the Sun and noticed that the spectrum, in addition to being graded from red to violet in the usual colours of the rainbow, was crossed by a number of dark lines. This mysterious result was not caused by a faulty spectroscope since

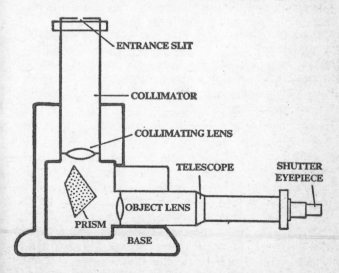

Fig. 3-2. The optical arrangement of a modern spectroscope

candle light did not show the same effect. Wollaston believed that the lines divided the spectrum into its "four colours". However, this explanation was incorrect and probably discouraged Wollaston from carrying out further work with his instrument, so preventing him from realising its great possibilities.

Even though Wollaston's work on the spectroscope did not bear fruit it would be unfair to judge him on this invention alone, significant as it was. He was regarded as the most skilful chemist and mineralogist of his day and he published papers on pathology, physiology, optics, crystallography, astronomy, electricity, mechanics and botany. In middle age blindness, along with numbness of his left arm, made it clear that he was suffering from a brain tumor and would shortly die. Far from abandoning his work, he set about dictating papers on his unrecorded scientific studies so that they could be published after his death. He had experiments carried out in a laboratory next to his sick room, and only a few days before his death was directing the progress of the work from his bed.

Slowly other workers took an interest in the spectroscope and began to experiment. It is well known that sodium compounds give flames an intense yellow colour; this can easily be seen by sprinkling salt on to a fire. If the flame of a Bunsen burner is coloured yellow by a sodium compound (this is called a sodium flame), and it is now used as a source of light for the spectroscope, then the spectrum is found to consist of only a faint continuous band of rainbow colour and, more distinctly, a few vertical lines. Most prominent by far of the lines of the sodium spectrum is a pair of yellow lines lying very close together. Other metals were used to colour flames—for example, iron, calcium, magnesium and copper—always more mysterious lines turned up. Each metal produced its own lines which were always in exactly the same part of the spectrum: sodium in the yellow, calcium in the violet, copper in the green, and so on. Sometimes there were a few lines, sometimes there were many.

In 1814 Wollaston's experiment of spectroscopically observing the Sun was repeated by a German optician called Fraunhofer. Like Newton, Fraunhofer was interested in perfecting the telescope on behalf of his employers, an optical firm in Munich. Again the mysterious dark lines appeared across the spectrum. Fraunhofer was a very capable optician and had made such an accurate spectroscope that he was able to count the lines: there were 576 in all. He charted them and identified them by letters but was unable to think of a reason for their existence. Fraunhofer quite correctly rejected Wollaston's theory that the lines marked the boundaries between different colours because many of the lines occurred in the middle of very prominent coloured portions of the spectrum. In the yellow, for instance, there was a pair of dark lines very close together to which he had given the identification letter D, which clearly marked no change of colour in that particular portion. He then tried a most significant experiment. He divided the slit of his spectroscope into two parts; the top half he illuminated by the Sun and the bottom half by light from a sodium flame. He found to his surprise that the dark pair of D-lines of the Sun corresponded exactly with the bright pair of yellow lines on the sodium flame. This is why the yellow lines of sodium are always referred to as D-lines. These two lines are so close together that only the most sensitive of spectroscopes will show them separated and they are most often seen as a single very easily observed yellow line.

It is surprising that Fraunhofer did not follow up this very striking result by seeing whether any other sources of light corresponded with the dark lines of the Sun. It was left to other workers to show that elements such as calcium, iron, chromium, zinc, copper and hydrogen all showed bright lines which corresponded with dark lines on the Sun's spectrum. In time very nearly all of Fraunhofer's 576 lines were matched up with the spectra of elements.

Two of the greatest workers in the early years of spectroscopy were Bunsen (who invented the Bunsen burner) and Kirchhoff. It was they who first discovered to what use a spectroscope could be put by showing that every element which they examined produced its own definite spectrum and, just as important, that this spectrum was characteristic of that element only.

Here then was an unmistakable way of recognising an element; it is in fact as unmistakable as the human fingerprint. Just as no two human beings have the same set of fingerprints, no two elements have the same spectrum. Moreover, the time taken to recognise an element by means of its spectrum can often take as little time as that required by a Scotland Yard detective to take a fingerprint. This was the basis of what we now call spectroscopic analysis. Since mixtures of substances show the characteristic lines of all the metals in a mixture, a glance at the spectrum is enough to tell us which metals the mixture contains. It is also a sensitive method of analysis: sometimes the high sensitivity can be troublesome. Sodium, for example, will show its D-lines when it is present in incredibly small amounts; mixtures containing one part in a thousand million of a sodium salt reveal the metal's presence. Since it is difficult to produce substances of such a high degree of purity that they do not contain tiny quantities of sodium, early scientists had great difficulty in discovering just what it was which caused the D-lines to be visible on all their spectra. So accurate an instrument is the spectroscope that it gives its name to substances of the highest standard of purity: an analyst calls a substance spectroscopically pure when the spectroscope shows there to be no impurities present.

Kirchhoff and Bunsen had together shown just how important an instrument the spectroscope could be.

But Kirchhoff had also carried out another fascinating experiment. It is interesting to note that five years before Kirchhoff gave details of this experiment in 1859, a student who had attended a series of Lord Kelvin's lectures in Glasgow had made notes which showed that Kelvin undoubtedly knew of this experiment from his own work. It seems that the honest Kelvin refused to publish this work because he believed it to have been carried out even earlier by a scientist named Stokes. Stokes, however, was just as retiring and modest. In the end the honour of being first to go to press must go to Kirchhoff, who, in any case, was working quite without any knowledge of the results of the British scientists.

Kirchhoff's experiment was to take a source of ordinary white light and to focus it on the slit of his spectroscope so as to produce the usual continuous spectrum. He next took a Bunsen flame and placed it between his source of white light and the spectroscope (Figure 3-3). He converted the Bunsen flame into a source of sodium light by pushing into the flame a piece of material soaked in a solution of common salt

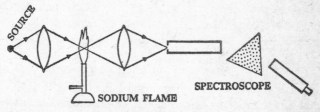

Fig. 3-3. Kirchhoff's experiment

and he then inspected his spectrum. He was surprised to find that in the yellow portion of the spectrum was a pair of *dark* vertical lines corresponding exactly with the D-lines in the Sun's spectrum. Kirchhoff immediately saw the reason for this. The sodium in the flame obviously acts in very much the same way as does a filter paper; light from the source corresponding with the D-lines is held back (or *absorbed*), as a filter paper holds back particles of solid; the rest of the light passes through unchanged as would a liquid through a filter paper.

Kirchhoff confirmed this conclusion by removing the white light source, at the same time still watching the dark lines. As the bright source was removed, leaving only the sodium flame, the bright background of the spectrum became dark. However, the dark D-lines were now revealed as yellow lines, due to the flame, standing out sharply.

Kirchhoff went even further with his experiments. He filled a glass flask with the vapour of sodium metal and placed it in between the white light source and the spectroscope; again there was a dark line in the yellow part of the spectrum showing that the sodium in the flask was absorbing part of the white light.

The same sort of experiment can be carried out with two sodium flames. Suppose that light from one of these flames is focused on to the slits of a spectroscope and that the second flame is placed between the first flame and the slits. It is found that if the second flame is cooler than the first, then the lines appear dark; if it is hotter, then the lines are brighter than ever. If the two flames are at the same temperature then the lines merge with the background and cannot be seen at all. Clearly when the second flame is the cooler it is absorbing light given out by the hotter one; when it is hotter it reinforces the light from the first; and when they are at the same temperature as much light is being absorbed as is being emitted.

Kirchhoff found that this type of experiment could be repeated with the other lines of the spectrum of sodium besides the D-lines, and that this behaviour was not limited to sodium: the lines of calcium, potassium, copper and other metals behaved in exactly the same way. A metal would always absorb or emit its own lines, and none other.

Kirchhoff was now in a position to bring about one of the first major triumphs of the spectroscope. At that time, in the middle of the last century, the Sun was still the remote and incomprehensible lord of the sky. It was known to be a vast distance away from us and to have a very high temperature. How could Man hope to know more of it than these few awesome facts? Except for the observations of its motions and the limited detail which could be seen through a telescope little was known of it; it seemed as though there was not the slightest possibility of ever discovering what the Sun was made of. But Kirchhoff's experiment was a sudden and immense leap forward in scientific achievement, for from it he saw how to explain the cause of the dark Fraunhofer lines in the Sun's spectrum, and at the same time, how to discover what substances were present on the Sun—93,000,000 miles away.

The hottest part of the Sun which we can observe is at its surface, which is a region called the *photosphere*. The photosphere is so hot that it emits only white light and its spectrum is continuous from red to violet. Surrounding the photosphere, however, is a layer of much cooler gases known as the *chromosphere*. The chromosphere contains the vapours of a number of elements and it is these elements which absorb parts of the spectrum of the photosphere. The resulting spectrum which we see is a continuous band broken by lines corresponding to the elements in the chromosphere. In this way, at this vast distance, we are able to say exactly what the outer regions of the Sun's atmosphere contain. This alone was a staggering achievement for the spectroscope in its very early history. But there was more for it to achieve. There were still a number of the lines which Fraunhofer had seen in the Sun's spectrum which could not be related to any particular element. Could it be that there was something in the chromosphere which did not exist on Earth? Or were there still elements on Earth to be discovered? We will leave these questions unanswered until a later chapter when we discuss some more of the achievements of the versatile spectroscope.

4

Simple Experiments with a Spectroscope

To produce a spectrum you need hardly any equipment: just a hose-pipe and the Sun—although the Sun can on occasions be more difficult to find than a piece of hose-pipe! However, a home-made rainbow in one's garden is not an easy sort of spectrum to control. A much more convenient form can be made by making a round bottomed flask filled with water act the part of a single large raindrop. If, in a darkened room, a narrow beam of light is shone on the flask, behind which is placed a white screen, a small circular spectrum can be projected on to the screen (Plate X).

Newton's crucial experiments on the refraction of different colours of light were carried out with the simplest of equipment: as we have seen he bought his first prism at a country fair. These experiments are simple ones to repeat, and inexpensive lenses and a prism will be quite adequate for the purpose.

If you come to the point of deciding to obtain a spectroscope for yourself, the choice of equipment is not so simple since both the cost and the size of a spectroscope vary a great deal and depend on the use to which the instrument is to be put. A hand-held tube no bigger than a fountain pen and useful for making a quick rough and ready analysis costs only a few shillings. A precision laboratory instrument with high quality prisms and lenses suitable for the highest accuracy observations can cost many hundreds of pounds. In both cases, however, Wollaston's arrangement for the very first spectroscope is followed. Since this arrangement is a very simple one the spectroscope is a relatively easy instrument to build in one's own home. No special tools are necessary other than those to be found in a normal workshop or tool-kit, but the optical equipment, that is to say the lenses and the prism, must be chosen with some care. An enthusiast who cannot buy or borrow a spectroscope will find in the appendix a useful guide as to how to set about building his own instrument. Even the simplest of spectra are very beautiful, and the effort involved is well worth while.

Even if you do not build your own spectroscope, most schools and laboratories have models which can be quickly set up for use. There are many simple experiments which can be devised to make interesting spectra observable. The easiest of all to obtain is of course the spectrum of white light. An electric light bulb is the most convenient source but better still, if it is available, is an arc lamp. If the white light is focused on to the slits at the eye-piece, there can be seen a perfect continuous spectrum from red to violet.

The next most convenient source of light is a Bunsen burner. By soaking a strip of asbestos in a solution of a salt of any metal and holding it over the burner the Bunsen flame can be made to burn with the characteristic colour of the metal. Sodium is the easiest metal to view first; only a very dilute solution of common salt is necessary to give a bright yellow flame and the spectrum will show the distinctive D-lines in the yellow. Only a good spectroscope with a very narrow slit will show these as two lines close together rather than a single wide line, or reveal the much fainter lines in the orange, green and other portions of the spectrum.

Potassium is another easy metal to observe, using clean heated asbestos soaked in potassium chloride solution. The first things to be seen are the yellow D-lines. This tells us something immediately: that the potassium (or the asbestos) is not pure but contains sodium. Even if a potassium flame is made by holding a platinum wire covered with hydrochloric acid and potassium salt crystals in the flame, the D-lines still appear. This confirms the well-known fact that potassium salts are very difficult to obtain pure and free from sodium. However, in addition to the D-lines, distinctive red potassium lines can be seen as well as lines in other parts of the spectrum. An interesting test of the sensitivity of the spectroscope is to blow cigarette smoke into a colourless Bunsen flame when it is quite easy to see both the yellow lines of sodium and the red lines of potassium due to the potash contained in the cigarette.

There is no limit to the metal solutions which can be examined with a Bunsen flame. Some of the more interesting metals to identify in this way are barium, calcium, copper, iron, manganese and zinc.

But the Bunsen flame is itself capable of giving what is probably one of the most beautiful of all spectra. There are two distinct parts to a roaring Bunsen flame: the inner and outer cones of burning gases. The small inner cone contains quite a number of different compounds of hydrogen and carbon and these too, like metals, are capable of showing their own spectra. If light from the bright tip of the inner cone is focused on the slit the spectrum will show some fascinating bands of colour in the blue and green. These bands are not at all difficult to obtain by simply using a butane cigarette lighter as the light source.

All the spectra mentioned so far are known as *emission* spectra because they result from a substance giving out, or emitting, light. Kirchhoff's *absorption* spectra, in which light is absorbed by substances, can be examined in just the same way as was done by Kirchhoff himself. Perhaps the simplest way of observing absorption is to take a white light source and place a piece of red glass in between it and the slit. Instead of a multi-coloured spectrum, all that is left is a narrow band of red. This is because the red glass absorbs all light except red, which it allows to pass unchanged. Different coloured glasses behave in exactly the same way, allowing only light of their own particular colour to pass.

We have seen how Kirchhoff caused flames and vapours to absorb light. Solutions too will absorb, and a very dilute solution of potassium permanganate will prevent narrow bands of light in the green and blue from passing from a bright white light source. As the solution becomes more concentrated the dark bands in the spectrum broaden and finally join together. When the solution is very concentrated it will cut out almost the whole of the light.

You can best carry out this experiment by placing a flask, or wine glass, containing water in front of the slit of the spectroscope; add a few drops of a concentrated solution of potassium permanganate and observe the change in the spectrum. Add more permanganate solution and repeat your observations. Try the same kind of experiment with solutions of other substances, such as copper sulphate and iron sulphate.

The reasons for the appearance of so many different colours, lines and bands in these spectra will not be obvious to you as you carry out your observations, but from later chapters you will be able to provide at least some explanations. Your results will perhaps guide you in devising other experiments. Certainly the work of the nineteenth-century pioneers is well worth repeating.

Remember that the spectroscope, as well as being a simple instrument, is sensitive and, at times, a seemingly frustrating one. Newton, Wollaston, Fraunhofer,

Kirchhoff and Bunsen had at least two qualities in common: care and patience. Without these they would not have progressed, nor given us the knowledge we use today. The young experimenter will need these qualities along with his spectroscope. Together, they will give some rewarding results.

5

Waves
of Light

In the early nineteenth century the spectroscope, as used by Wollaston and Fraunhofer, was still at its baby stage of development, and in order to understand just how it became the indispensible aid to astronomers, biologists, chemists and physicists there are certain topics which we must examine more closely. Wollaston and Fraunhofer had shown that the spectrum of sunlight was crossed by a number of dark lines. Kirchhoff and other scientists had shown that the positions of these lines corresponded exactly with the lines emitted by heated chemical elements such as sodium, calcium, iron, magnesium and many, many others. So, in some way or other, light is related to these elements. It soon became clear to the *spectroscopists* (as they were later to be called) that if they could discover only a few of the vital clues relating light and the atoms of elements then a whole new field of science might be opened to them. In between Wollaston's discovery of the dark lines in 1802 and the present day these vital clues have been uncovered and every day new and exciting discoveries are made in the field of spectroscopy.

In order to understand the steps by which this

progress has been made we must first examine more closely in this chapter what we mean by *light* and in a later chapter what we mean by *atoms*.

What do we know about light from our every day experience of it? First, we must be quite definite about the fact that we cannot *see* light as it travels. Of course you can see this page, but you cannot see the rays of light which must be passing from the page to your eyes. In a dust-filled room it is often possible to see the paths of the Sun's rays from a window into the room, but what you are seeing are not the rays themselves, but reflections from the dust particles which are illuminated by the rays. Nonetheless, the fact that the dust particles which are illuminated all lie in straight lines does tell us something about light: that it travels in straight lines. If this were not the case then light would not cast shadows, nor could the cinema projector throw huge images of films on to the cinema screen.

We also know that light is reflected from bright shiny surfaces; a mirror is, of course, the simplest example of this occurring in every day life, but it is also worth noting that even the darkest and roughest of objects do reflect small amounts of light. Another property of light is that it is bent when passing from one transparent substance to another (Plate I) and that, as Newton showed, different colours of light are bent, or refracted, by different amounts depending on their colour.

So much is known about light from experience of the world around. Some quite simple experiments are necessary to reveal other properties of light. If a sensitive thermometer is placed in any of the colours of the spectrum of the Sun then the thermometer shows an increase in temperature. This tells us the most important fact that *light is a form of energy,* just as heat and electricity are forms of energy. Also it is found that if a flask from which all the air has been removed is placed in the path of a ray of light then the light passes through the flask undisturbed. In other words light (and hence light energy) can pass through a vacuum. Light travelling from the Sun to the Earth over a distance of 93,000,000 miles travels through what is almost a vacuum over the whole of its journey outside the Earth's atmosphere. What is more, light reaching us here on Earth began its journey from the Sun about eight minutes ago. The exact speed of light has been calculated and has been found to be 186,000 miles per second. By comparison with light, our modern astronauts are moving at a snail's pace!

Most of these facts about light were well known in the middle of the seventeenth century, and it was at this time that the argument began among scientists as to *how* light travels. The argument was to continue for three centuries and still provides material for discussion today. *How* can light energy travel across many millions of miles, at a fantastic speed, through empty space, through a sheet of solid glass and then be split up into colours? Newton, needless to say, attempted to provide an answer and he put forward what is known as the *corpuscular theory*. In this theory Newton suggested that light is made up of tiny particles called corpuscles which move at speeds far greater than bullets, but like bullets, they carry energy. These corpuscles presumably can be bounced off shiny surfaces and in this way light is *reflected*. Also they can pass through transparent solids or liquids at different speeds and are *refracted*. In order to explain the colours of the spectrum we must assume that light is made up of different sized corpuscles which correspond to different colours; since they are of different sizes they are refracted by different amounts by a glass prism and so a spectrum is formed.

However, it became clear that the corpuscular theory was not an entirely satisfactory one. For one thing the theory required that light should move faster through glass than through air; many years later, when more advanced techniques made the experiment possible, it was shown that the opposite was true. So the corpuscular theory went out of favour. But even in Newton's day there were plenty of alternative theories as to how light travelled. The most important of these, and one which we will go into in a little more detail, is the *wave theory* which followed from some suggestions made by a Dutch scientist, Christiaan Huygens. Young and Fresnel developed Huygens' simple suggestions and proposed that light might travel in waves.

Fig. 5-1. A train shunting shows a simple form of wave motion

You can see the simplest sort of wave motion in action by watching a train shunting a long line of wagons (Figure 5-1). The first wagon to be struck by the engine travels to the second wagon and strikes it. The first wagon now bounces back to its original position whilst the second wagon strikes the third. The process is repeated along the whole line of wagons, one at a time until the last one is struck and is shunted off. Sound travels by this kind of wave motion. The sound of your neighbour's voice is carried to your ear by the molecules of air bumping into each other in much the same way as the train's wagons. This kind of wave motion is known as *longitudinal* because the wagons or the air molecules move in the direction in which the wave is sent out.

A different kind of wave motion comes into operation if you take a length of rope, tie it to a post and then flick the rope so that a "hump" travels from your hand to the post (Figure 5-2). A similar thing happens

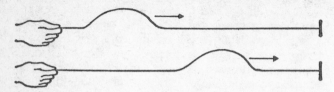

Fig. 5-2. Wave motion in a rope

if you throw a stone into a pool to make ripples travel over the water's surface. You will notice an interesting similarity in these two examples. Although the "hump" travels along the rope, the rope itself does not move towards the post but moves at right angles to the direction in which the hump moves. And although the ripples move across the water's surface, the water itself merely moves up and down. You can see this still better by putting a cork into the water and noticing that the ripples do not move the cork away from the stone but cause it to bob up and down. This kind of wave motion is called *transverse* because the rope and water molecules move at right angles to the direction in which the wave is sent out.

Young and Fresnel suggested that light is a transverse wave motion. In the case of the shunting wagons you will see that the wave motion moves in one straight line, and in the case of the pool of water that it moves across a surface (that is, in two dimensions). Light waves are assumed to be three dimensional and to spread out in all directions in space from the source of light.

So much for the theory of how light travels by wave motions. We must now investigate whether this theory satisfactorily explains all we know about the properties of light. For example, is it possible to say that light moves by means of waves and is also capable of travelling in straight lines? The answer to this question would only be yes if the waves of light were very very tiny indeed; in fact we shall see just how minute these waves are. Can waves be reflected? Without any doubt they can. Sound waves are often reflected from the sides of steep valleys and give rise to what we call an echo. Water waves too can be reflected and you can watch this happening by dropping a pebble into a bowl of water and noticing how the waves are reflected from the sides of the bowl. Water waves can also be refracted; this happens when a wave at sea passes from deep to shallow water and the wave wheels at an angle in much the same way that light is bent when it passes from glass to air. The colours of the spectrum can also be explained by giving different sizes of waves to different colours; since this topic is so important to our understanding of how the spectroscope works we shall return to it later.

The wave theory, as we have so far discussed it, is really neither better nor worse than the corpuscular theory. If it were only possible to show that waves behave in a way which would be impossible for corpuscles (or tiny particles of light) then there would be really strong evidence for the wave theory. Now it was known that waves can, under certain conditions, *interfere* with each other. Thus if you take two pebbles and drop them into a bowl of water you will see that at certain points the waves from the different pebbles reinforce each other and where they cross form a wave which is about twice the height of a non-reinforced wave. At other points the water is motionless where the waves have cancelled each other. This phenomenon is called *interference* and it is known to happen also with sound and radio waves. Light waves, therefore, should show interference.

Sitting in your room it is possible to hear certain sounds through the open window which come from a source which you cannot see. Thus you can hear a motor car horn although it need not necessarily be in your line of vision. The sound waves are said to be *diffracted* to your ear because they spread sideways through the open window. You can watch water waves being diffracted when a wave of sea water overtakes a boulder on the sea shore. You will notice that there is a space of sand behind the boulder which is untouched by water, and the wave is eventually bent in behind the boulder; the smaller the boulder, or the bigger the wave, then you will notice how much easier the wave diffracts around the obstacle. If sound and water waves show diffraction, then light too, if it is a wave motion, should be capable of behaving in the same way.

It was a scientist named Young who set out to show that light waves would interfere with each other. He caused light of one colour (such as the intense yellow of a sodium lamp) to pass through two slits so that each slit became a source of light. Young placed a screen behind the slits and saw that at its centre, where light from the two slits overlapped, there was a dark shadow. In other words the waves of light had cancelled and were showing interference. This was excellent news for the supporters of Huygens' wave theory because Young's experiment showed that so far as interference goes light motions behave like the motions of sound and water waves.

What now of diffraction? A Frenchman named Poisson set out to show that if waves of water can be diffracted round a boulder then, if light is a wave motion, it too could be diffracted round an object of suitable size. For his source of light he took a tiny illuminated pinhole and placed about two yards away from it a circular disc the size of a sixpence. A further two yards away he put a screen and he then examined the shadow of the disc. Sure enough, at the centre of the shadow was a bright spot: the waves of light were being diffracted round the edge of the disc, like sea waves round a boulder, and illuminating the centre of the screen. The supporters of the wave theory were triumphant, and Poisson took his remarkable result to the Academy of Science in Paris. Poor Poisson! The Academicians told him that his result was absurd, and only when he had persuaded a friend to repeat his experiment in order to establish the diffraction of light beyond any doubt was his experiment taken seriously.

The wave theory differed from the corpuscular theory in one very important point: it required that the speed of light should be slower in glass than in air and, as we have seen, this prediction was correct. However, in spite of all this mass of evidence in favour of waves of light, there were some problems which left doubts in the minds of inquisitive scientists. The wave motions we have mentioned, other than light, all require some substance to carry the waves. Sound needs air, sea-waves need water; what then carries light? The answer cannot be a simple one since it is known that light can pass through completely empty space. How can light be a wave motion with nothing available to carry the waves? The evidence in favour of light's being a wave motion was too strong to allow the theory to be discarded and so the philosophers were forced to propose that all space must contain a mysterious medium: the ether.

The existence of the ether was an assumption for which there was no experimental evidence whatsoever. How can there be a substance which fills the whole of space, including vacua? We cannot see it nor can we measure it in any way. In 1883 Michelson and Morley tried to calculate the speed of the Earth as it travels through the ether. The surprising answer they managed to get was $0/0$, which in mathematical language means *anything*! Having to assume the existence of the ether was indeed a thorny problem, and yet without it waves of light would have no means of being carried through space.

And so, although the wave theory seemed to reign supreme because it explained so many of light's properties, there was cause for reasonable doubt that it satisfactorily explained in every way all that was happening. Many years after the controversy between the theories of Newton and Huygens, round about the beginning of this century, various most exciting experiments were carried out which gave rebirth to the idea that light was after all made up of corpuscles. It is not necessary for our understanding of the way in which light is used in the spectroscope to describe these experiments. However, it became clear that in part of its behaviour light acts as though it is a wave motion, and in others as though it is made up of corpuscles. Light is now believed to have what is called a dual nature and the corpuscles behave as though they were little groups of waves.

For three hundred years scientists have discussed and sometimes even quarrelled about the exact behaviour of light. Some men, such as Huygens and Poisson, have been laughed at because of their beliefs, but when these beliefs have been substantiated by good reasoning and careful experiment our store of scientific knowledge has been increased. In the case of the subject with which we have so far dealt in this chapter we have seen that there is no clear cut answer and that, in the end, the result is a compromise.

In order to apply this knowledge to the working of a spectroscope it is necessary to use some of the results of both theories. To be able to know something more of the extent of the spectrum and its range of colours, the wave theory and the ways in which we measure waves are important.

When a pebble is thrown into a pond the water waves produced spread out smoothly: the crests of the waves follow the troughs outwards in ever increasing circles. It is very easy to imitate these crests and troughs by repeatedly flicking a rope which is tied to a pole; in doing this you will see that "humps" follow "hollows" in the rope from your hand to the pole. We believe that, although we are unable to see them, light waves also travel in just this sort of way with crests regularly following troughs. We can very conveniently represent any one of these wave motions by drawing a wavy line (Figure 5-3). The distance between crests, or between troughs, is called the *wavelength* of that particular wave motion. Thus waves in a saucer of water can have a wavelength of a few millimetres and waves at sea can have a wavelength of several metres. Sound waves commonly measure a few feet. Light waves too have been measured but have been found to be very much shorter than any of the examples we have so far discussed.

We have seen that the wave theory suggested that white light was split into different colours because the waves of the different colours of light were of different sizes and were refracted by different amounts. Measurements of the wavelengths of various colours of light have shown that this is the case and that red light has a longer wavelength than blue light (Figure 5-3); intermediate colours have intermediate wavelengths.

The number of red wavelengths which pass into your eye in any second must be less than the number of blue wavelengths. The number of wavelengths passing

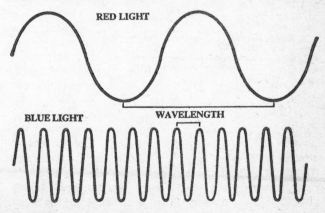

Fig. 5-3. The wavelength of red light is greater than that of blue

a point in any second is known as the *frequency* of the wave motion. So red light has a smaller frequency than blue light.

A. J. Ångström was a Swedish scientist who took an interest in the Sun's spectrum of dark lines. He decided to measure the wavelengths of the strongest of these lines and since the wavelengths of all kinds of light are so very small, he invented a new unit of measurement so that he could express his answers more simply. Ångström's new unit was one ten-millionth of a millimeter or 0.00000001 cm. This tiny unit was later called after Ångström and is signified by the letter Å or A.U. The wavelengths of the various colours of the visible spectrum are:

Table 1.

Red	7,600—6,200 Å
	(0.000076—0.000062 cm.)
Orange	6,200—5,950 Å
Yellow	5,950—5,600 Å
Yellow—green	5,600—5,400 Å
Green	5,400—5,000 Å
Blue—green	5,000—4,700 Å
Blue	4,700—4,300 Å
Violet	4,300—3,800 Å

6

The Atom

We now know how light behaves when it passes through the prism of a spectroscope. Most of this knowledge of the behaviour of light was familiar by the middle of the nineteenth century, and by that time it was becoming quite commonplace to recognise the presence of sodium, calcium, iron and other metals by their spectra. Later the spectra of non-metals were discovered: gases such as hydrogen and oxygen can be made to show dark absorption lines in the same way as do metals, but the methods of obtaining the spectra are more complicated than the extremely simple ways we have so far discussed.

It was soon noticed that in the case of certain substances the thin spectral lines had a certain pattern of regularity and it was even possible to invent mathematical equations which forecast the positions of these lines. Hydrogen, for instance, has a spectrum whose lines have a pattern which can be described by a relatively simple mathematical equation. Some groups of substances which are similar in appearance and properties also show similarities in their spectra. Thus sodium and potassium, which are both soft, reactive

metals and which form similar compounds, both show
in their spectra pairs of lines very close together. In
the case of sodium the bright pair of D-lines is in the
yellow, and in the case of potassium there is a similar
pair in the red.

Obviously there must be a very good reason why
one metal gives out light of one wavelength while another metal produces light of a different wavelength.
If we could discover what this reason is then perhaps our spectra would be capable of giving us a whole
lot more information than the simple identification
fingerprint. In order to investigate this we must look
more closely into the structure of matter and discuss
in what way substances are built.

As to what is the smallest particle of matter has been
a major scientific problem for thousands of years. If
we sliced up a grain of sand with a microscopic knife,
could we go on slicing each piece into smaller and
smaller parts indefinitely, or would we arrive at particles which can be sliced no more? Greek philosophers attempted to answer this question by supposing
that matter consists of tiny particles called *atoms*
(from the Greek, α, meaning not, and $\tau\epsilon\mu\nu\omega$ meaning
I cut). They supposed that atoms could not be cut up
into smaller pieces by any means at man's disposal.
This theory was of no great value until John Dalton
introduced some novel ideas which were to be the
foundations of modern chemical theory.

Dalton was born in 1766. When he was only twelve
years old he began teaching and soon opened a school
in his native village of Eaglesfield in Cumberland. Later
he obtained a post as mathematics and chemistry
teacher at Manchester New College, and in 1807
he published his famous Atomic Theory.

In this theory Dalton proposed that the atoms of a
pure "elementary substance", or *element*, were per-
fectly alike in size and weight and that they could be
neither created nor destroyed. He further supposed

that the atoms of elements could combine to form "compound atoms" or *molecules*.

As examples of elements we have hydrogen, carbon, oxygen, chlorine and sodium; it is not possible for us to break these elements down into simpler substances, no matter whether we act on them with acids, burn them in air or use any chemical means whatsoever. However, we can convert these elements into more complicated substances quite easily. Thus if we burn carbon in oxygen we form molecules of carbon dioxide, and if we explode hydrogen with chlorine we form molecules of hydrogen chloride. At high temperatures these compounds can be separated into their elements once again. We depend upon this fact when we soak asbestos in sodium chloride solution and heat it in a Bunsen flame, otherwise we should not be able to see the sodium D-lines with our spectroscope.

Dalton's picture of the atom was a very simple one. He imagined it to be something like a tiny billiard ball. Different elements would consist of billiard balls of different weights and sizes. He realised that these billiard balls must be so tiny that one could never hope to see them, even with the help of a miscroscope. It is as well to remember that even today the atom cannot be seen in spite of such huge magnifiers as the electron microscope.

For a hundred years Dalton's picture of the atom was shared by other scientists. Indeed, it was a very useful picture to have since it succeeded in explaining how elements behaved, and how they reacted to form chemical compounds. What made chemists first suspect that atoms might not be quite so simple as solid little balls was a whole series of experiments using electricity. These were begun by Michael Faraday. Faraday, like Dalton, had very humble beginnings to his life. He was the son of a blacksmith; at thirteen he became an errand boy to a bookseller and bookbinder. Bookbinding was not his main interest in life, however; he had begun to take an interest in chemistry and physics, and one day he wrote to Sir Humphry Davy saying that he wished to enter into the service of science. Davy was impressed by the boy and made him a laboratory assistant at the Royal Institution. By 1827 Faraday had risen to be Professor of Chemistry at the Institution.

He carried out a number of experiments by passing an electric current through certain liquids. He showed that there was a relationship between matter and electricity and he discovered some very important and now famous laws which relate the two. It was found that under certain conditions atoms can behave as though they were particles of electricity.

The real truth lay in the fact that atoms are not like the solid billiard balls which Dalton had imagined but that they were themselves made up of even tinier particles. Far from being solid they were found to consist mainly of empty space! The first of these tiny particles to be discovered was the *electron*. The electron is very, very tiny and weighs about one two-thousandth as much as the lightest atom, hydrogen; one atom of hydrogen weighs less than a millionth of a millionth of a millionth of a millionth of a gram! By comparison with our every day use of weights the mass of the electron is unimaginably small. More interesting than the discovery of its weight was the realisation that the electron has a negative charge of electricity and that it can travel at great speeds carrying its negative charge along with it. Some knowledge of the electron is very important to our understanding of how the spectroscope works since, as we shall see, it is the behaviour of the electron which gives rise to all spectra.

Other constituents of the atom were later discovered. Since we know all atoms to be electrically neutral they must contain something which has a positive charge equal to that of the electron. The particle which carries such a charge is called the *proton*. The proton is much bigger than the electron and weighs roughly the same as a hydrogen atom. Every atom must always have the same number of protons and electrons so that it can remain electrically neutral. There is a third important particle in the atom's make-up and this is called the *neutron,* but it carries no electrical charge; by weight it is very similar to the proton. There are numbers of other particles which have been discovered, but these need not concern us at the moment.

The next question we must ask ourselves is, how are the electron, the proton and the neutron arranged in the atom? It is a question which is not at all easy to answer and which puzzled the minds of many scientists in the early years of this century. There is no *exact* answer to the question but we can form a rough picture to guide ourselves. Dalton's picture of atoms as billiard balls was far from exact, but it was of immense value in understanding the very important problem of how atoms take part in chemical reactions.

The first thing that we know is that the electrons are separated from the protons and the neutrons. The protons and the neutrons together form what is called the *nucleus* of the atom: (*nuclear energy* is energy derived from the nucleus). Since the protons are positively charged then the nucleus has the same kind and the same amount of charge. The electrons move in space around the nucleus. We can now draw a picture of the atom as a guide to our understanding of its behaviour, remembering as we do so that in reality an atom cannot be seen and, even if it could, would not remotely resemble our picture. When we draw a quick sketch of a tree we represent all of its green leaves by a roughly circular black line on a piece of flat white paper. Even though this drawing is in reality nothing like a tree, we can certainly recognise what the drawing is supposed to represent. So it is with our "atomic" drawings.

The simplest of all atoms is that of hydrogen (Figure 6-1). In its nucleus there is a single proton and nothing else. Since its nucleus has one positive charge, there must be one electron travelling in space outside the nucleus. We represent the path of this electron by a circle and call it the *orbit* of the electron. We imagine that the electron moves around the nucleus in much the same way as an astronaut moves in orbit around the Earth, although on the atomic scale, if the Earth represented the nucleus, the astronaut would be a great deal more than a few hundred miles above the ground.

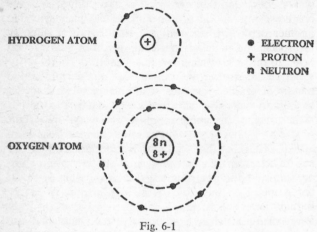

Fig. 6-1

Other atoms have more complicated arrangements. Thus, the oxygen atom has eight protons and eight neutrons in its nucleus; there are also eight orbiting electrons, and six of these move in orbits which are further from the nucleus than the remaining two. The other hundred or so known elements are built up in the same way with additional electrons associated in larger orbits. Sir J. J. Thomson, who discovered the electron, thought of the positions of electrons in the atom as being situated rather like currants in a bun. In its way, this gave a successful picture of how electrons were spread around the atom. It was Niels Bohr who conceived the idea that electrons might move in orbits—though this idea too is only a schematic picture.

Supposing you were to tie a stone to the end of a rope and to swing the rope round and round your head; by doing so you would be giving the stone energy. You know this to be true since if the rope were to break the stone would fly off at a tangent and possibly, by virtue of its energy, do damage to a window pane. In the same way an electron orbiting its nucleus possesses energy and the amount of this energy depends on the size of the orbit. For our astronaut to move into another orbit, farther from the Earth, he must supply his space capsule with more energy from his fuel in order to move himself.

There are several ways in which we can increase the energy of an electron; one easy way is to supply heat to the atom. We do this to a sodium atom when we put asbestos soaked in sodium chloride into a flame. Other ways of supplying energy are, for example, by applying a high voltage electric discharge to the atom, by allowing high frequency electromagnetic waves to fall on it, or simply by causing another fast moving atom to bump into it. The result of this application of energy is that the electron jumps into another orbit. Usually the electron which suffers this change is one of those in the outer orbit, although an electron nearer the nucleus can be affected in the same way.

When an electron has been shifted in this manner it does not remain in its new orbit but usually jumps back to its old orbit. To do this it must release its new found energy. *It is this release of energy which enables us to link up our knowledge of light with the structure of the atom*. Light, as we know, is a form of energy and this energy depends on the wavelength (or colour) of the radiation. It so happens that the energy released by an electron in returning to its original orbit takes the form of radiation which has the wavelength of visible light. In other words, the yellow light we are seeing from a sodium flame is a sign that energised (or "excited") electrons of sodium atoms are returning to their original orbits and in doing so are giving off radiation with a wavelength of about 5900 A.

The amount of energy released by an electron in jumping from one orbit to another in a sodium atom, even though we are able to see this energy in the form of light, is very tiny indeed. But just as there is a limit to the number of times we can slice up pieces of an element with an imaginary knife, so there is a limit to the way in which we can divide up energy. We can compare changes of energy to the changes of height above the ground which a man can achieve when he jumps up a flight of stairs. If the height of each stair is one foot, then by successive leaps, he can reach 1, 2, 3, . . . etc. feet above his original position at the foot of the stairs. But in no way can he arrive at a height of 1¼ or 2⅓ feet because there simply are no stairs to hold him in such positions. This is also the manner in which energy changes are made. Each "stair" or "packet" is called a *quantum* and energy changes always take place in definite amounts of whole quanta: never by halves or thirds of quanta.

And so when an electron in a sodium atom changes its orbit it always takes in or gives out a definite and fixed number of quanta. The numbers of quanta involved depend on which electron has moved and to where it has moved. Since in an atom such as sodium there is a limited number of electrons as well as a limited number of possible changes, so the jumps of energy are restricted. Suppose there were a number of bare-footed men (who represent the electrons in an atom) who were each running up and down their own set of stairs (representing the possible energy changes of an electron). Now suppose some careless carpenter were to come along and drop tintacks over most of the stairs. Because our electronic men are barefooted they will now be able to leap only from the stairs without tintacks and so their energy changes in jumping to the ground are always by definite and fixed amounts. The stairs without tintacks can be compared with the orbits of electrons and the change of energy of a jumping man to the energy given out by an electron when it moves from one orbit to another.

With a sodium atom the most frequent change is one which produces energy in the form of radiation of the wavelengths corresponding to a pair of narrow lines in the yellow of the spectrum. There are other energy jumps possible within the sodium atom and the radiations in these cases correspond to other lines. The jumps which involve larger amounts of energy change are responsible for radiation of the shorter wavelengths. So when an element shows lines in the blue end of its spectrum, electrons are making bigger energy jumps than they would have if the lines had turned up in the red.

To return yet again to our picture of electrons in an atom as being like athletically-inclined gentlemen, if a flat sloping board were placed over the stairs and if there were no tintacks to hinder their progress, they would now be able (if they were sufficiently athletic) to jump down from any particular height they chose without any restrictions whatsoever. If an electron were able to behave in this abandoned fashion it would be able to give off light of all colours of the rainbow. However, in an atom an electron's movements are restricted in the same way as those of a jumping man on tintacked stairs. Only sharp energy changes are possible and these are revealed on a spectrum as very narrow lines.

We have seen that the spectrum produced by changes taking place in an atom gives rise to bright lines like the yellow pair in the spectrum of sodium. This is exactly what we would expect if electrons were moving from orbits of high energy to those of a lower energy; the energy they lose is given out as light. How then can we explain the dark lines which occur in the Sun's spectrum and which Kirchhoff found when he caused white light to pass through sodium vapour? The answer is that the reverse of what we have just

described is taking place. When white light passes
through sodium vapour the electrons of a sodium atom
are very willing to receive energy which will cause them
to jump into higher orbit. The energy they require is
in the yellow wavelengths and so they "steal", or
absorb it, from the white light. The rest of the white
light passes on unchanged and what we see in our
spectroscope is the usual spectrum of white light but
with a dark narrow gap in the yellow showing that
energy has been removed by sodium atoms. We now
see more clearly why Kirchhoff's explanation of the
dark lines in the Sun's spectrum is correct. White light
from the hot surface of the Sun, the photosphere,
passes through the many different elements in the
cooler outer chromosphere. Some of the energy of this
white light is "stolen" by the electrons of all the
different atoms in order that they can jump up into
different orbits. The spectrum we then see is crossed
by dark lines which correspond to all the different
energy changes which have taken place. Every atom in
the Sun's chromosphere undergoes energy changes of
one kind or another and we are able to recognise it by
its spectrum.

The most obvious use of the spectroscope is that,
by looking at lines of the spectrum we are able to detect elements with great certainty—even though they
may be on the Sun at a distance of 93,000,000 miles.
Now that we have linked the behaviour of light energy
with the structure of the atom it is easy to see that the
uses of spectroscopy need not necessarily be limited
to the identification of elements. By carefully studying
the spectral lines of many elements, chemists and
physicists have been able to learn a great deal about
the electrons of the atom, since the positions of these
lines show just how the electrons have moved. Remembering the minuteness of the electron you can see
what a remarkable achievement this is. We shall
discuss more of the uses of spectroscopy later, but this

brief example will serve to show just how subtle a tool it is.

So far we have talked about two types of spectra. The first is the type given by white light and shows a smooth gradation over the whole of the spectrum through the various colours of the rainbow. This type is called a *continuous* spectrum. The second type we have discussed in detail; this is the *line* spectrum. The line spectrum arises from changes taking place within an atom of an element such as hydrogen, oxygen, sodium or mercury. There is a third type known as a *band* spectrum. In appearance it looks like a set of bands stretching across the spectrum; these are dark and sharp at one end and gradually fade away at the other. High-powered spectroscopes show that the bands are in fact made up of narrow lines; there are many lines at the dark sharp end and they reduce in number where the bands fade. A band spectrum has been shown to be the result of changes, not within an atom, but within a molecule: that is, in a compound formed by the union of two or more atoms. Molecules such as nitrogen, N_2, cyanogen, C_2N_2, and water, H_2O, all give their distinctive band spectra.

In the same way that we can use line spectra to give us information about atoms, we can use band spectra to tell us something of molecules. We shall see in a later chapter how widely band spectra are used by modern scientists to give them all sorts of once unsuspected and hidden information about Nature at work.

7

Tools of
the Trade

Although Wollaston's original arrangement of prism, lenses and slit is still the basic way in which a spectroscope is constructed, the development of the instrument has been by no means static. Since the spectroscope has a wide variety of uses, improvements have been made to certain parts of the apparatus to make it more suitable for the particular task that has been chosen.

Even before early spectroscopists could begin to look at spectra they had to develop methods of heating to high temperatures the samples of substances which they wished to analyse. Only at these high temperatures would the substances be vaporised, and the changes in the electron structure of the atoms which we have discussed would take place. When temperatures are too low electrons simply remain in their original orbits, and without energy changes within the atom there is no possibility of light energy being given out.

The first and most simple method of heating was to use the Bunsen flame along with a suitable way of holding the substance in the flame. However, only a relatively small number of substances reach temperatures in the Bunsen flame which are high enough to give spectra. For example, a piece of rock containing ore is usually unaffected when placed in such a flame. Other methods had to be devised whereby very high temperatures could be reached quickly and easily. Electrical methods were the obvious answer, and a number of these were invented which answered particular purposes ideally.

A historical description of these methods of heating elements to high temperatures should of course begin with the flame method, since it was the one which the first spectroscopists used. In spite of the fact that the Bunsen flame failed to reach the high temperatures of which electrical methods were capable it was not abandoned as a spectroscopist's tool. For many important reasons some investigations require the fairly gentle heat of the flame, and *flame spectroscopy* has become an important science, which we shall discuss later.

A hot Bunsen burner flame burning a mixture of ordinary coal gas and air has a temperature in the region of about 1500°C. Air, however, contains four parts of nitrogen to only one of oxygen. Since nitrogen does not take part in any combustion process in the flame, it tends to cool the flame down, and by using air with reduced amounts of nitrogen in it, or simply by using oxygen, we can get a hotter flame. It also helps if we use another fuel rather than the fairly gentle coal gas, which, after all, is rarely expected to do much more than roast a side of beef. Coal gas is a mixture of such gases as hydrogen, methane and propane. Hydrogen burning with oxygen alone will give a much hotter flame than coal gas and air; it can give temperatures of about 2500°C. Acetylene and oxygen raises the temperature to about 3000°C (oxy-acetylene welders and cutters depend on this fact), whilst the hottest flame of all is produced by burning the gas cyanogen with oxygen, when 4000°C is reached. Oxy-cyanogen flames, however, are difficult to control and have not found the same uses in industry as have oxy-acetylene flames.

Having got a suitably hot flame, we are now faced with the problem of putting the substance in which we are interested into the flame. Most flame spectroscopy is carried out on substances which are soluble in water and the easiest way of introducing sodium into a flame is one we have mentioned many times: that of soaking a sheet of asbestos in a solution of a sodium salt and holding it in the flame. However there are drawbacks to this method. If the asbestos contains traces of impurity such as salts of other metals then these too will show up in the spectrum. We can get over this difficulty by holding the salt on the end of a piece of platinum or porcelain; a little hydrochloric acid usually helps to make the salt more volatile. Since platinum, porcelain and hydrochloric acid do not themselves affect the spectrum much, this is a better method. Its chief drawback is that we must continually remove the platinum or porcelain to replenish the salt so that we can go on seeing the spectrum. What we really require is a method that will continuously feed the salt to the flame. The solution to this problem is rather a surprising one: the scent spray. If we put into the scent bottle a solution of salt and cause it continuously to spray the solution into the gases on their way to the burner we then have an ideal way of steadily supplying substances to the flame. The original inventor of the scent spray would probably be surprised if he could see how the device which he had originally intended for some lady's dressing-table is being used so effectively in a chemical laboratory.

Improvements have also been made in the designs of Bunsen burners used in flame spectroscopy, and these, combined with the best methods of introducing substances into the flame, make very effective spectroscopic tools.

Electrical methods of heating have enabled 65 of the 90 elements known in Nature to have their spectra examined. The first method we shall discuss is the *electric arc*. The electric arc has been used as the chief means of obtaining spectra ever since 1876, when a dynamo known as the Gramm dynamo was invented. An arc is formed when an electric current is made to flow between carbon rods whose ends are placed close together. When an electric potential of about 50 volts is used, a brightly luminous flame or discharge, at a very high temperature, occurs where the current passes between the two rods. Temperatures which can be reached by this method approach 4000°C.

The bright light given out by a discharge between carbon rods is put to very good use in the cinema projector which uses an electric arc as its source of light capable of throwing the image of a film on to a screen a few hundred feet away. Such an arc requires continual adjustment to keep it burning brightly and this can be made automatically, but in early cinemas the projectionist who forgot to make the appropriate adjustments during crucial points on the film was liable to become unpopular.

For use in spectroscopy the electric arc may consist of two carbon rods, or of rods made of any other suitable material, such as silica. The rods are usually about a quarter of an inch in diameter. A small pile of the substance to be examined is placed just under the gap between the rods so that it lies in the region of highest temperature when the current is passed. Alternatively a hole can be made in the end of one of the rods and the substance placed inside the hole. The spectroscope is pointed at the discharge in the same way as it is pointed at the flame, in order to record the spectrum.

The arc is so bright that it is dangerous to look at it directly and it should never be observed except when the eyes are protected by smoked glass. With higher voltages precautions should also be taken against electric shock and it is usual to see linoleum or rubber floors in a room where an electric arc is used.

But the use of an electric arc is not restricted to a laboratory. Portable varieties are made so that mineralogists can take their equipment out on location. Some prospectors even manage to rig up generators driven by their motor car engines to work their electric arcs. In this way, when they are perhaps hundreds of miles away from civilisation, they have a very convenient method of identifying precious metals in rock samples.

Another method of raising metals to high temperatures is the *electric spark*. In this case a very high voltage is made to pass between the two rods of the metal. An induction coil and a condenser are used to produce the high voltages necessary; and when the induction coil is started up brilliant sparks pass between the metal rods, and this is the source of light which is used by the spectroscope. From 10,000 to 25,000 volts is the usual voltage range employed with the electric spark and once again painful electric shocks can be had if proper precautions for insulation are not taken.

One of the most important uses of spark spectroscopy is in the examination of smelted metals and of metal alloys. However, the use of the spark is not necessarily restricted to dealing with metals. Substances which do not normally conduct electricity can be ground up with powdered carbon and pressed into the shape of pellets; these pellets are then substituted for the metal rods. It is also possible to arrange that a spark can be made to pass between drops of liquid, so that examination of solutions of metallic salts is also possible with this method.

We have already mentioned how Kirchhoff filled a glass globe with the vapour of sodium and how he used it to learn something about the absorption spectrum of sodium. It was later found to be possible to heat vapours and gases contained in glass tubes by passing a high voltage electric current through the tube. This apparatus is called a discharge tube. The usual

Plate I. Refraction of beam of light in a tumbler of water

Plate II. An old print showing the Sun's spectrum being formed on a screen by a prism, and being viewed through a second prism to recombine the colours

Plate III. Sir Isaac Newton

Plate IV. Research spectrometer made by Hilger and Watts

Plate V. William Hyde Wollaston

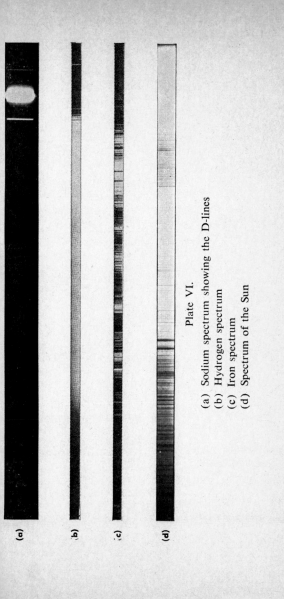

Plate VI.

(a) Sodium spectrum showing the D-lines
(b) Hydrogen spectrum
(c) Iron spectrum
(d) Spectrum of the Sun

Plate VII. A spectroscope being used to compare a Bunsen flame with that of a candle

Plate VIII. Robert Wilhelm Bunsen

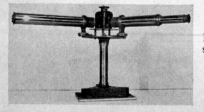

Plate IX. A spectroscope, built about 1875, with a liquid prism

Plate **X.** An artificial circular rainbow formed by a ray of light passing through water in a round bottomed flask

Plate **XI.** Lockyer's apparatus for observing the spectrum of the Sun and comparing it with spectrum of an iron arc

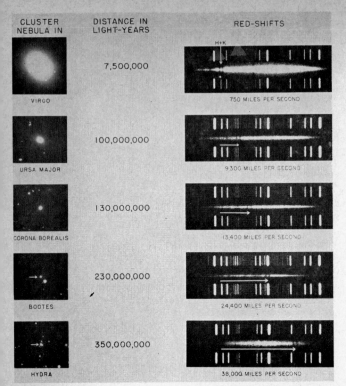

CLUSTER NEBULA IN	DISTANCE IN LIGHT-YEARS	RED-SHIFTS
VIRGO	7,500,000	H+K / 750 MILES PER SECOND
URSA MAJOR	100,000,000	9,300 MILES PER SECOND
CORONA BOREALIS	130,000,000	13,400 MILES PER SECOND
BOOTES	230,000,000	24,400 MILES PER SECOND
HYDRA	350,000,000	38,000 MILES PER SECOND

Plate XII. Humason's remarkable spectrum showing the red-shift of calcium lines. The left hand photographs show the galaxies in question with their distances from us in light-years. The right hand spectrograms show the red-shift and the speed with which the galaxies are moving away from us. It is the hazy central band in the centre of each spectrogram which is the spectrum of the galaxy; the upper and lower lines in each case are merely for comparison purposes. The white horizontal arrows show the extent of the red-shift as the speed of recession of each galaxy increases

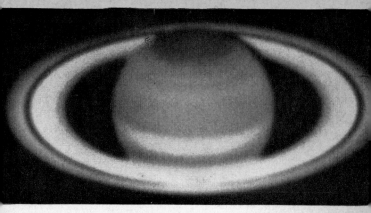

Plate XIII. Saturn and its rings

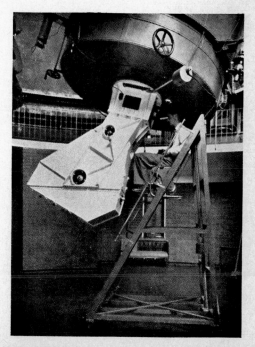

Plate XIV. A telescope fitted with a spectrograph

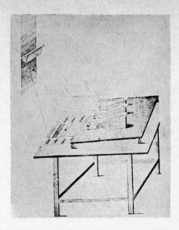

Plate XV. The equipment with which Sir William Herschel proved the extension of the solar spectrum into the infra-red

Plate XVI. A modern quartz and glass spectroscope

method is to construct a tube of the shape shown in Figure 7-1. Two metal electrodes are sealed into opposite ends of the tube. The tube is exhausted of all air and a small amount of the gas or vapour under investigation is then allowed to enter before the tube is finally sealed off. Hydrogen, nitrogen, iodine vapour or water vapour are examples of substances which can be used in a discharge tube. When a high voltage (about 10,000 volts) is applied to the tube, a current passes along the tube and the gas inside it glows. The glow is brightest at the narrow part of the tube, A. It is this portion which is examined by the spectroscope.

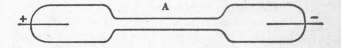

Fig. 7-1. A discharge tube

The colours of glowing gases in discharge tubes depend on the gas itself, how little gas there is present in the tube, and what voltage is applied. There is a wide range of colour and it is this effect which is used in night signs for advertising. Neon gas is often used and has given its name to neon signs. Piccadilly Circus would have been a different place had it not been for the invention of the discharge tube.

So much for the ways in which substances are heated to high temperatures. As these methods were perfected, so were the various parts of the spectroscope which make use of the light given out by the heated substances. The most important part of the spectroscope is its prism, since it is this which is responsible for splitting up light into its various colours. More work and time has been spent on improving prisms than on any other part of the spectroscope.

The effect of a prism on the light which passes through it is to cause the light, particularly violet light, to be bent through a considerable angle. The amount of bending which takes place depends on the quality of the glass of which the prism is made. Some types of glass are more useful than others depending on what the spectroscopist is looking for. Really accurate spectroscopes can be as much as several yards long in order that the different parts of the spectrum are separated as completely as possible from each other. Since light is bent in the spectroscope, the collimator and the telescope must be set at an angle to each other. The result, in the case of high-powered spectroscopes, is a rather bulky instrument of quite an awkward shape, and sometimes cumbersome to use. Spectroscopists therefore set out to build an instrument which would occasionally make life easier.*

What was required was a simple prism which would not bend the light in its path from the source, but would nevertheless still split it into its component colours; the problem was solved by Amici, who used an arrangement of different prisms. Three prisms are required in all; two are made of crown glass and one of flint glass. The flint glass prism is cemented by transparent cement between the other two as shown in Figure 7-2. The glass of each prism is such that the paths of the differ-

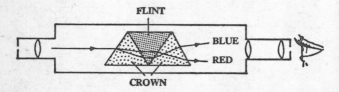

Fig. 7-2. Direct vision spectroscope

* Spectroscopists are not the only scientists who think of their own comfort. Astronomers have been known to make their telescopes rather more complicated and bulky so they could sit inside a pleasantly warm and sheltered room and yet have the business end of the instrument outside in the cold night air. If at all, the problem is reversed for the spectroscopist: he often has to shield himself from the heat of his flame!

ent coloured light are as shown, and reach the eye of
the observer in a direct line from the light source. The
slit, lenses and prisms are usually mounted in a simple
and handy brass tube; the result is known as a *direct
vision spectroscope*. It is very useful for making quick
examinations of flame spectra. Its chief disadvantage
is that it does not separate the different parts of the
spectrum as well as a normal instrument and the lines
are crowded together.

The direct vision spectroscope is easy to handle and
quick to use, but as spectroscopists learned more about
spectra they found that they needed an instrument
which separated the spectral lines from each other as
much as possible. To do this they were willing to put
up with the spectroscope's awkward shape. They even
looked for a substitute for the prism which might give
better results than a prism. It was not long after the
invention of the spectroscope that a suitable alternative was found. Fraunhofer discovered that there were
so many lines in the absorption spectrum of the Sun
that a prism did not separate them sufficiently for him
to be able to count and letter them all. (Remember
that Fraunhofer counted 576 lines in the Sun's spectrum.)

We have already discussed how light is diffracted
round objects. It was known that a set of parallel slits,
arranged like miniature bars across a tiny window, also
caused light to be diffracted and to be fanned out into
a spectrum. A set of very fine lines drawn on glass or
some other transparent surface has the same effect and
is known as a *diffraction grating*. The path of light
through a diffraction grating is shown in Figure 7-3.
Fraunhofer realised that here was a way of spreading
out the Sun's spectrum so that he could catalogue the
absorption lines more easily. In 1814 he made his first
diffraction grating in a very clever fashion by stretching fine silver wire across a frame. He used about 200
wires to the centimeter. Later diffraction gratings were

made by ruling lines with a diamond cutter on a glass
plate. It was even found possible to make reflecting
diffraction gratings by using very high precision ma-
chines to rule as many as 5,000 lines per centimeter
on metal surfaces. Because of the extreme precision of
the work involved in preparing these surfaces diffraction gratings of this type are very expensive; however,
it is possible to make celluloid casts of the originals
costing only a few pounds. Unfortunately there is a
limit to the number of casts which can be made from
each metal grating since with use the metal lines lose
their sharpness. If carefully made, the first fifty or so
replicas are excellent.

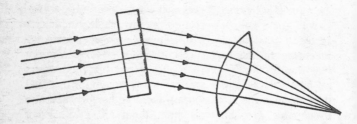

Fig. 7-3. The path of light through a diffraction grating

The great advantage of a diffraction grating is that
it spreads the spectrum and enables us to separate portions which otherwise would be difficult to observe.
However, it has a disadvantage compared with the
prism. The ruled lines prevent some of the light falling
on the grating from passing through, just as the flow of
water passing through a water grating is partly restricted by the bars of the grate. At the same time,
some light passes straight through the gaps in the grating without being diffracted. Only the light passing
close to the edge of a line is diffracted and is useful
to the spectroscopist (Figure 7-3). The result is that
the spectrum from a diffraction grating is much fainter
and much more difficult to observe than that from a

prism. Sometimes we can overcome this difficulty by making the source of light brighter; for example, we might increase the temperature of the electric arc or increase the amount of solution we are feeding through our scent spray to the flame. Yet there is always a limit to the amount of brightness which can be achieved in these ways. Often we have no control whatsoever over our light source; this happens when we are looking at the spectrum of a distant star. So on some occasions the diffraction grating can be a great help and can supply a lot of new information, but on others we must rely on the prism.

There is one most important improvement which was made to spectroscopes in the late nineteenth century. All the earliest observations of spectra were made either by looking directly at light from the prism by eye with the help of a telescopic eye-piece, or by casting an image of the spectrum on to the screen. Both of these methods have their drawbacks. The human eye is a very sensitive organ but it is not so perfect that it never makes mistakes, particularly where colours are concerned. Two spectroscopists could find that they disagreed on what they saw in the same spectrum. When disagreement over a spectrum occurred the argument could always be settled by using the second method: that of projecting the spectrum on to a screen, as both Newton and Wollaston had done. But even this method was not altogether satisfactory. Spectra were not always easy to see in detail on the screen, particularly when only tiny amounts of substances were available to experiment with, and when they gave off only a weak light.

The answer to the problem came with the invention of photography; without it, spectroscopy could never have become of such importance to scientists. Instead of a screen, a photographic plate was placed in position to receive the spectrum. Since photographic emulsions are very sensitive to light the spectra of even very weak light sources could be recorded and, better still, the photographic plate with its picture of the spectrum could be kept for ever, used to make comparisons and to settle arguments.

The spectroscope with the photographic plate attached is called a *spectrograph* and the photograph of a spectrum is known as a *spectrogram*. Nowadays spectrographs are made with fittings attached so that the plate can be slid into a holder and removed to the darkroom for developing without stray light reaching the plate. The inside of the case of a spectrograph is always carefully painted black since any reflected light will fog and spoil the photograph.

A photographic plate has certain advantages over the human eye. It is possible to manufacture photographic emulsions which are very sensitive to particular portions of the spectrum: some emulsions, for example, are especially sensitive to the red end of the spectrum. Therefore if a spectroscopist is interested in a substance which shows a set of lines in the red he will use a red-sensitive plate, and be able to photograph more than his eye could possibly see.

Some spectral lines are so weak that the human eye cannot see them directly under any circumstances. There is no reason, however, why a spectroscopist should not leave his spectroscope pointed at his faint source (such as a star) for many hours in order to make sure of recording the weak lines.

Yet another advantage of a plate is that a bright line in a spectrum is seen on the developed photograph as a dark image; a less bright line has a less dark image. By comparing the darkness (or density) of these images some most important information can be deduced; this we shall discuss later.

In this chapter we have talked about some of the many changes and improvements which the spectroscope has had during its hundred and fifty years or so of existence. The examples given are some of the more important ones but there are still many others. Wollaston's simple spectroscope remains basically unchanged; the adaptations and improvements still being made show what a wonderfully versatile instrument it is.

8

The Telltale
Fingerprint

A detective uses a fingerprint as one of his most important aids to identify criminals; in the same way, a chemist or a mineralogist uses a spectrum to identify substances. Just as no two people have identical fingerprints, no two substances have identical spectra. Unfortunately for the detective, apart from being a foolproof means of identification, the fingerprint tells him nothing else about the owner of the fingers. For example, it does not tell him whether his criminal has blue eyes, a broken nose, or a hot temper; it does not even tell him whether he is dealing with a man or a woman. A chemical substance does not have any of the bodily or mental characteristics of a human being, but it does have chemical and physical properties which, in their way, are just as interesting, and, to the chemist and physicist, just as important. One of the most remarkable facts about a spectrum is that when properly interpreted, it tells the spectroscopist many of these properties. It is rather as though the detective were also a never-failing palmist who could read a person's character from the lines of a fingerprint. In this chapter we will discuss some of the ways in which a spectroscopist uses the lines of a spectrum to give him information of an amazingly wide variety.

The first and simplest use to which a spectroscope was put was that of the identification of elements. Even before the invention of the spectroscope early chemists had used the colours which certain elements give to flames as a guide to identification. The yellow flame of sodium, the blue of copper and the green of barium are all easy to see and recognise. But this is a rough and ready method, which can be used when the substance contains plenty of these elements. If we have a mixture of elements in a substance things are not quite so easy, because the colours can hide one another. Also, only a few elements give to the flame a colour which is strong enough to be detected by eye. Supposing we had a mixture of sodium chloride and barium sulphate in a flame. In this case the yellow light from the sodium would be so intense that the green colour due to barium would be completely swamped. If we looked at the flame through a spectroscope this difficulty would be completely resolved, since we should be able to see in the spectrum the lines due to sodium and those due to barium which are unmistakably separated from each other. Easiest of all to see of the lines of these two elements would be the yellow lines of sodium and the green lines of barium. We might have chosen elements which have characteristic lines lying quite close together and difficult to identify by eye. This problem is easily solved by using a spectrograph to photograph the spectrum and, with the help of a wavelength scale drawn up in Ångström units, we can fix the lines and their parent elements without any shadow of doubt.

Quite complicated mixtures can be analysed in this way and mineralogists rely on the spectroscope to give them the composition of rock samples containing as many as ten or twenty different metals. The spectroscope is also a very sensitive instrument and metals present in only tiny amounts can be identified. As small a quantity as 1/100,000,000th of a gramme of sodium can be detected by using a spectrograph. Lithium, calcium and strontium are examples of other elements which can be identified when only tiny amounts are present in a sample.

Some of the elements which have simple atoms with only a few electrons have only a few lines, but heavier ones, where there are more electrons capable of making energy "jumps", have many more lines. To identify an element it is usually necessary to know only its most intense and easily seen lines, as in the case of the D-line of sodium. As examples of other lines which occur in a spectrum here are the wavelengths at which a few of the lines of sodium and barium are seen and the corresponding colours of the lines:

Sodium			*Barium*	
A			A	
6161	orange		*6142*	*orange*
6154	orange		5536	yellow-green
5896	*yellow*	}D-lines	4934	blue-green
5890	*yellow*			
5688	yellow		4554	blue

The strongest lines for each element are shown in italic. Altogether over 100,000 lines of different elements have been identified but if one were to count all the faint lines the number would be nearer a million. Obviously a spectroscopist can carry around the wavelengths of a very few of these lines in his head, and so very comprehensive *Wavelength Tables,* of which the above lines of sodium and barium are a sample, have been prepared. Wavelength tables are the spectroscopist's dictionaries and enable him to pinpoint any element.

Since a complicated substance like a rock sample contains a large number of elements its spectrum looks very confused and a considerable amount of skill is required by a spectroscopist to sort out all the lines he sees. In spite of the fact that the chromosphere of the Sun contains a large number of elements, J. N. Lockyer noticed that there was a group of lines in the spectrum of the chromosphere of the Sun which did not correspond with those given by any element in the laboratory (see Plate XI). This led him to suspect that the Sun contained an element which was unknown on Earth. He called this element "helium" (meaning Sun-element). Years later, at the turn of the century, helium was found to be present in the mineral cleveite, in natural waters such as those found at Bath, and in the gas fields of Ontario and Alberta.

Lockyer's discovery, one of many similar ones about that time, has given spectroscopy another valuable use: that of discovering a new element. Towards the end of the last century, there was still a large number of elements which were suspected but never found. Scientists immediately realised that the spectroscope was capable of giving them new and exciting discoveries and set to work. The laboratory notebook of Sir William Crookes, showing how he first recorded the observation of a new element in March 1861, can still be seen in the Natural Science Museum, South Kensington. Crookes had become interested in the element selenium (discovered in 1817) and made observations of its flame spectrum. This is what is written in his neat handwriting in the little notebook (Se is the chemical symbol for selenium):

"Small portion of some residues from distillation of Se (containing much Se) placed in a blowpipe flame. Observed a bright green line. Once or twice very strong, at other times difficult to see at all. Tried whether it was Se. Some pure Se in flame gave regular bright green bands alternately light and dark close together but no definite sharp green line . . ."

Crookes' careful observation of the bright green line had for the first time revealed the element thallium.

About thirty elements were discovered by means of the spectroscope and some of them can still only be found with great difficulty using any other means. It is interesting that many of the names of elements were given because of their most brilliant spectral lines. Examples of these are rubidium (red), thallium (green), caesium (blue) and indium (indigo).

The lines of the spectrum of each element are all of different brightness; some are very intense and others are very faint. Some of the faintest lines are only seen at all when the sample being examined contains a high proportion of the element. When there is a high proportion of element then the bright lines become brighter still. When a mixture containing barium is examined by a spectroscope the green line is seen to be much brighter than in a mixture containing half as much barium (although not necessarily twice as bright). It was soon realised that here was a possible method of measuring not only *which* element a sample contains but also *how much* of that element. If we know that only certain lines are to be seen and that these lines reach only a particular brightness when more than a certain amount of element is present, then we have a quick ready-made method of analysing a mixture without going into the intricate and sometimes long procedure of chemical analysis.

To show this method at work we can take the element zinc as an example. We must first prepare mixtures which contain different amounts of zinc. A suitable zinc compound is zinc oxide, and it must be mixed with an inert substance (that is to say, a substance which will neither affect nor confuse the spectrum of zinc): quartz is one such substance. The zinc oxide and quartz are pulverised together so that we have different mixtures containing between 0.01 and 80 per cent of zinc (pure zinc oxide contains 80 per cent).

If we now put each mixture separately into the electric arc and examine it with a spectroscope, we shall find considerable differences in the spectra. That is what we are likely to find for each different percentage of zinc:

0.01 per cent.	Three faint blue lines appear and disappear intermittently.
0.1 per cent.	The same three lines appear and sometimes disappear.
1.0 per cent.	The blue lines are faint but steady. Flashes of a red line appear.
5.0 per cent.	All the red and blue lines are strong and steady.
10.0 per cent.	The red line is now much brighter than the blue lines.
80.0 per cent.	Very similar to the 10 per cent sample.

If we now have a rock sample containing a number of metals and we wish to know the exact amount of zinc, then all we have to do is to pulverise it and compare it with the spectra of our prepared mixtures. The percentage of zinc present will then be the same as that sample which gives the most similar spectrum. Since mixtures containing between 10 and 80 per cent zinc show little change in their spectra it might be necessary, when we have substances of high zinc content, to dilute the substance by pulverising it with more rock.

We can then fix its zinc content by more accurate and more reliable methods than observations by eye. Basically, the method is the same as that just described. Spectrograms are made of the mixtures containing exact known amounts of zinc. When a mixture contains large amounts of zinc then the photographic image of the spectral lines are much darker than when only a little zinc is present, so that by measuring how dark (or how *dense*) any particular line is, we have a guide to how much metal is present in the mixture. Very accurate instruments are available to measure the density of the spectral lines; these are called *densitometers*.

The principle of the densitometer is to shine a light

through the spectrogram on to a photocell. The action of light falling on a photocell is to cause a current to pass through an electric circuit which can be made to work a galvanometer. So by watching the needle of the galvanometer it is possible to tell how much light is passing through the spectrogram. If the light is made to pass through any particular line of the zinc spectrogram, then less light will pass through a dense line than passes through a less dense one. By comparing the line of a spectrogram having a known amount of zinc with that of the unknown sample, it is possible to determine the amount of zinc in the unknown sample with a high degree of accuracy. Any metal can be measured in this way and once the spectrograph has been scaled to measure any particular element, or *calibrated,* the method is both speedy and efficient.

The amounts of elements present in mixtures can also be determined by *flame spectroscopy.* The flame, used as the source of light, is usually a mixture of a suitable inflammable gas such as hydrogen or butane (now well known as cigarette lighter fuel) mixed with oxygen and nitrogen. The metals are introduced into the flame as solutions of their salts in water using a scent spray in the manner described in Chapter 7. In this case, however, the spectrum is not observed by eye or recorded on a spectrogram but is measured by a photocell which replaces the eye-piece of the spectroscope. The light from any individual line of the spectrum can be made to fall on the photocell, and the brightness of the line is recorded in just the same way as with the densitometer. This again is a very accurate way of measuring quantities of metals and it does away with the necessity of taking and developing a spectrogram. Unfortunately not so many elements give flame spectra as arc spectra, since the temperatures of flames are lower than those of arcs, so that this method has a restricted use.

There is another factor which is important in measuring the intensity of the lines of a spectrum. This is that the brightness of the lines depends completely on *how* the metal is heated to the high temperature at which it gives off light. Although the lines of an arc spectrum of a metal are at exactly the same wavelengths as in the flame spectrum of the metal, the brightness and numbers of lines which are visible will be quite different. Also, a hot flame will give much brighter lines than a cool flame. Therefore, it is important for the spectroscopist to remember to use always the same source of light at exactly the same temperatures when he is carrying out an analysis.

Using the spectroscope to examine hundreds of rock samples collected from every land, it has been possible to estimate the average composition of the rock crust of the Earth. This tells us what any particular rock is most likely to contain.

The most common elements are:

	Percentage		Percentage
Oxygen	46.5	Calcium	3.6
Silicon	27.6	Sodium	2.8
Aluminium	8.1	Potassium	2.6
Iron	5.1	Magnesium	2.1
		Titanium	0.6

We see at a glance from this table that any piece of rock we pick up is almost sure to contain oxygen and is very likely to contain silicon too. The remainder of the elements not mentioned in this table, such as manganese, chlorine and copper, make up about 1 per cent of the Earth's crust. Lead is present to about 0.002 per cent, and gold and silver even less than this. This leaves little doubt as to why these last two are called precious metals.

As examples of what particular members of the Earth's crust contain we might look at granite and clay; notice the large amounts of silica (silicon oxide) in them.

	Granite	*Clay*
Silicon oxide	74.3	71.1
Aluminium oxide	14.4	12.5
Iron oxide	1.1	6.0
Calcium oxide	0.6	0.9
Sodium oxide	1.8	2.2
Potassium oxide	6.6	1.6

There is one other interesting method of measuring amounts of metals in substances—a method which has been perfected and put to good use only during the last two or three years. This method is derived from Kirchhoff's explanation of the reason why the spectrum of the Sun consists of dark lines crossing a bright background rather than brightly coloured lines crossing a dark background, as is the case with the emission spectrum of a metal. The reason, as we have discussed, is that light from the hot photosphere at the Sun's surface is absorbed by the elements in the cooler chromosphere. Kirchhoff showed that in the same way light from a sodium lamp is absorbed by a cool sodium flame and the D-line appears as a dark line crossing the yellow part of the spectrum.

Nowadays it is possible to make lamps which give out the characteristic light of many metals such as zinc, copper, aluminium and calcium. If this light is passed through a flame containing sprays of the corresponding metal, then the dark lines across the spectrum are seen. In exactly the same way as in flame spectroscopy, the intensity of the dark lines can be measured and used to analyse how much metal a particular substance contains. For various reasons this method is often more suitable for measuring tiny amounts of metal than is flame spectroscopy. One example of its use is in medicine; human blood contains, among other things, important compounds of metals in very small amounts. If the blood does not contain sufficient quantities of any particular metal, as a result of a bad or faulty diet, then diseases develop. The absorption method of determining metals is very suitable for investigating solutions of blood; using it, as little as 2 parts in 1,000,000 of zinc can be estimated, and so the exact cause of a disease due to a metal deficiency can be very quickly discovered.

All the experimental techniques we have discussed so far in this chapter have been concerned with identifying elements and measuring them in quantity. We originally drew the comparison between the spectroscopist and a spectrum, and a detective and a fingerprint. The identification of his quarry is as far as a fingerprint takes a detective in his investigations, and we have seen that the spectroscope fulfils its ability to identify elements with great ease. The spectroscope's ability to measure quantities of elements can be compared with a detective's being able to guess a man's weight by studying his fingerprint. To suggest that a very clever police officer could deduce some information about a man's weight by studying the lines of his fingers would be absurd, but a spectrum, remarkably, can tell us something about the inside of an atom. The ability of spectroscopy to probe into the secrets of some of the most minute particles of Nature is one of its most startling achievements.

Looking at the spectrum of an element such as iron, which has a large number of lines, seems to suggest that the lines are randomly situated across the wavelength scale without any sense of order. However, this was later discovered not to be the case. The clue to the fact that there was some order to the arrangement of lines came only after close examination of the simplest of all elements, hydrogen. Hydrogen has in its nucleus only one proton, and outside this it has one electron. Since there are a restricted number of energy "jumps" which this one electron can make there are relatively few energy changes within the atom, and so relatively few lines in the spectrum of hydrogen. A close investigation of this spectrum showed that there were five different groups of lines. A number of scientists set about inventing mathematical formulae which would forecast the exact positions of the lines in these five groups in terms of their wavelengths. Soon satisfactory mathematical relationships were discovered, and it was seen that every single line fitted into a definite pattern. This new knowledge enabled mathematical equations to be invented which helped to explain the lines in the spectra of all known elements from hydrogen to uranium. This was one of the most remarkable triumphs of spectroscopists, for with these equations they were able to discover more about how electrons behaved inside the atoms and what minute energy changes were taking place as a result of the movement of these electrons. So spectroscopy is capable of telling us detailed information about some of nature's particles which are so small that even with the most powerful microscope the human eye will never be able to see them.

It has already been mentioned that in addition to the line spectra of elements there are found to be band spectra due to compounds such as water, H_2O, carbon monoxide, CO, and nitric oxide, NO. These band spectra are very close sets of lines, sometimes crowded together in a dense mass, and sometimes fading away so that they are difficult to see. In the same way that mathematical equations have been invented to explain the lines of elements, so have equations been found to explain the bands of compounds. Again these equations give us some fascinating information.

Just as is the case with line spectra of elements, band spectra can be used to identify compounds. In the electric arc and spark most compounds cannot resist the high temperatures to which they are raised and so decompose, or break down, into their component elements. The temperature of the Sun too is so hot that even in the cooler outer chromosphere we expect to find only atoms. However, some compounds can exist at fairly high temperatures; when an arc is passed between carbon electrodes the spectrum does not reveal a blank spectrum but instead, some very interesting bands. These are due to the combination of the carbon with oxygen and nitrogen of the air to form carbon monoxide and cyanogen, and the bands of these two compounds are seen in the spectrum.

At lower temperatures such as those of a flame (say 2000°C) there are large numbers of compounds which exist and give band spectra. Every flame which burns oxygen with hydrogen or any other fuel containing hydrogen (such as petrol) gives a spectrum showing the bands of the water molecule, H_2O. A hydrogen flame into which a solution of a copper salt has been sprayed shows beautiful blue spectral bands of copper hydride, CuH.

One of the most interesting features of the band spectra of flames is that they help to discover not only new molecules, but also molecules which, at one time, it was thought could not possibly exist. Even a simple flame of oxygen and hydrogen, without anything else added to it, shows something of interest in its spectrum, for, in addition to bands of H_2O, there are bands which have been shown to be due to the molecule OH. Everyone who has studied a little chemistry will realise that a molecule made up of one atom of oxygen and only *one* of hydrogen is a very unlikely combination. Most chemistry masters impress on their pupils some simple rules of *valency*; one of these is that *two* hydrogen atoms always combine with one oxygen atom. Many chemistry masters are very annoyed when their pupils try to break this simple rule. But the flame spectrum clearly shows that, under certain conditions, these rules can be broken.

However, it would be unwise to press such an example without realising that these unlikely molecules have very special properties. Most important is that they are exceedingly reactive; OH very quickly combines with an atom of H to form a water molecule, and all chemistry masters are therefore justified in saying that one oxygen atom always prefers to have two hydrogen atoms attached to it. Because OH is so reactive it never lives long in nature—usually only a fraction of a second. By the time the gases from the Bunsen burner reach the top of the flame, all the OH has disappeared.

There are many other examples of this kind of unlikely molecule. If the gas butane is burned in a Bunsen burner and the spectroscope is pointed at the outer cone of gases then it is possible to identify the spectra of H_2O, CO and OH. If, however, the spectroscope is moved to point at the bright inner cone of the flame then a whole new group of bands of colourful greens and blues appear. These are due to the molecules C_2 and CH which are so reactive and live for such short fractions of a second that they are lost before they reach the outer cone of the flame.

Flames, discharge tubes and other sources of light reveal wonderful ranges of these interesting new molecules and provide a large field of examination for the chemist. Not only can he study atoms and compounds and their concentrations, he can also discover how they react with each other. We have already mentioned a simple example: that of the combination of OH and hydrogen atoms in a flame. The reaction which takes place is:—

$$H \quad + \quad OH \quad = \quad H_2O$$

Other reactions which can be studied are:—

$$H \quad + \quad O \quad = \quad OH$$
$$N \quad + \quad O \quad = \quad NO$$
$$Cu \quad + \quad H \quad = \quad CuH$$

The chemist can deduce not only where and when these reactions take place, but also how and at what speed.

A molecule such as water has a simple formula, H_2O. However, the idea of thinking of water as consisting of two hydrogen atoms hooked onto oxygen atoms in this fashion:—

$$H — O — H$$

is far too simple. In fact the water molecule is not a straight one; the atoms are arranged in space as though they were at corners of a triangle and a truer (though still not an accurate) picture would be:—

$$O$$
$$H \qquad H$$

But neither the electrons nor the nuclei of the atoms are stationary. For one thing the electrons are capable of making energy "jumps", as we have discussed. Also the hydrogen atoms vibrate backwards and forwards, toward and away from the oxygen atom, rather as though they were connected to it by a rubber band or springs. Even more confusing, the whole molecule can rotate in space, perhaps like a boomerang or a Mexican bolas flying through the air. Surprisingly, the lines of a band spectrum give the spectroscopist information about these complicated movements. Without the help of spectroscopy it is unlikely that any chemist or physicist would have dreamed of the idea of suggesting that these minute atoms and parts of atoms lead such agitated lives.

It was not long after it was realised that the dark lines across the Sun's spectrum were due to the absorption of light by elements that it was discovered that molecules can absorb light in the same way. As early as 1862 the Royal Society was receiving news that when light was passed through liquids such as alcohol and glycerine, solids such as fluorspar and ice, and gases such as hydrogen and oxygen then the spectrum of light was crossed by dark bands. Today absorption spectroscopy is one of the most important applications of the spectroscope, and the first thing that is usually done to a newly prepared substance is to measure its absorption spectrum. The range of this spectrum, however, is not restricted to the wavelengths of visible light; nor for that matter are many of the spectra we have already discussed. There are mysterious invisible spectra, which will be described in another chapter, which are most important, and which are put to very good use; the principles involved in getting information from these spectra, however, are basically just the same as in the case of visible light.

First it was found that the absorption spectrum of a molecule such as water is just as useful as a fingerprint, as is the line spectrum of an element such as sodium. It can be used to identify and to measure amounts of the molecule. What was more exciting to chemists was that different molecules often showed similar, though not identical spectra. For example there were certain similarities between the bands of the absorption spectra of carbon dioxide, acetone and formaldehyde. The chemical formulae of these substances are:

Carbon Dioxide	CO_2
Acetone	$(CH_3)_2 CO$
Formaldehyde	H_2CO

Each of these three substances contains the same pair of atoms, carbon and oxygen joined together to form a group: CO. Different compounds containing the CO group were found to show similar bands in their spectra. When a compound contains other groups such as OH, CC and CH, characteristic bands show up in the spectrum due to these groups. Here, then, is a way of deciding how a molecule is built; with skill, a spectroscopist can judge from his absorption spectrum how atoms are joined within a molecule.

Sometimes the laboratory work of a scientist seems

very remote from our own day to day existence. This is not the case with absorption spectroscopy. Suppose that when you are ill you visit a doctor, who takes a test sample of your blood. In order to diagnose a suspected illness he will send your blood sample to be analysed. Whereas some years ago it would have taken a skilled analyst many hours to analyse the blood, with the help of a spectroscope it will take him minutes. Having diagnosed your illness the doctor might recommend an operation. Your safety throughout the operation will depend upon carefully purified antiseptics (analytically tested) and stainless steel forceps and scalpels (the stainless alloy itself had to be analytically controlled). The waste from the operating theatre will eventually find its way to a sewage farm; before it can be poured out into the river the sewage must be analytically tested and shown to be free from infection. As a final example of the great variety of use to which a spectroscope is put we will show that, surprisingly enough, it can be used as a thermometer to measure temperatures which are well outside the range of a common mercury and glass thermometer. Again we can take the flame as the example and suppose that we wish to measure the temperature of the gases in the flame. The principle involved is one which has been quoted several times in this book: that of the absorption of spectral lines discovered by Kirchhoff.

The spectroscope is pointed at a lamp which gives off a bright, white light and whose brightness can be varied by altering the electrical voltage across the lamp. The flame is placed between the spectroscope and the lamp so that light shines through the flame. Into the flame is sprayed sodium chloride solution, and the spectroscope is focused so that it views the D-line. It is found that when the flame is hotter than the lamp, the spectrum shows a bright yellow D-line against a darker background; when the lamp is hotter than the flame light from the lamp is absorbed at the D-wavelength and the spectrum now shows a dark line against a brighter background. However, when the lamp and flame are at the same temperature the D-line disappears altogether. All that is necessary is to adjust the lamp voltage until the D-line disappears, and we know that the lamp and the flame have equal temperatures.

There are a number of instruments available to measure the temperature of the lamp, although they would be quite useless for measuring the temperature of the flame directly.

Of course it is often impossible to use a lamp behind every source of light; we cannot manœuvre the Sun or a star to suit our purposes. But there is yet another way of measuring temperatures. The lines of a spectrum have a certain width and brightness which depend on how hot is the source of light. Using the appearance of these lines the temperature of the source can be calculated. This is an invaluable aid to astronomers seeking more information about the universe, and we shall discuss more of the ways in which they employ a spectroscope in the next chapter.

These have been only a sample of the capabilities of the spectroscope. The mineralogist uses it as a never failing identifier of metals; the analyst who requires high accuracy in his measurements can have complete faith in its ability; for the chemist it provides a huge new laboratory of investigation of chemical compounds and hidden reactions; with it the physicist probes the secrets of the minutest atom, and the doctor can use it to diagnose human diseases. These are remarkable achievements for one scientific instrument.

9

Messages from the Stars

Astronomy, with good reason, lays claim to being the oldest of sciences. Every man who has looked up at the sky on a clear night has wondered and speculated at what lies on these worlds separated from us by such vast distances of space. Until the nineteenth century, astronomers had to content themselves with making observations of the movements of the planets and the stars. Their telescopes told them a few detailed things about our nearest neighbours, such as the existence of vast craters on the Moon and of the rings around the planet Saturn; but beyond that there was little which they could say about the nature of these worlds.

Space had proved to be an almost impenetrable barrier, and there was no optimism amongst scientists that anything could possibly change the situation. In the early years of the nineteenth century the French philosopher Auguste Comte said that one of the problems which man would never be able to solve was that of the composition of the stars. He assumed that because we could not reach out and touch these heavenly bodies we would be forever incapable of saying which atoms and molecules they contained and how these atoms and molecules behaved. But Comte was not

aware of the power of the spectroscope and its ability
to receive information from any body which gives
out light. It was only a few years after Comte made
this statement that he was proved wrong, for Kirchhoff then began to interpret the absorption spectrum
of the Sun's chromosphere and the meaning of the
Fraunhofer lines. As we have seen, it was soon not
only possible to say precisely which element were present on the Sun, but also to identify some which had
not been found on Earth. A whole new and exciting
chapter had suddenly opened up for astronomers, for
this was the beginning of the science of astronomical
spectroscopy.

The principle of the astronomical spectroscope,
which records such delicate messages over the immense
distances of outer space, is that of a spectroscope
mounted on a telescope; the spectroscope merely replaces the eye of the telescope's observer.

As the technological skill of astronomers and spectroscopists improved it became possible to examine
stars which were much farther from us than our neighbouring Sun; the bright star Sirius, for example, was
investigated, and then much fainter stars. Nowadays
it is possible to obtain the spectra of stars which are
a hundred million times fainter than Sirius.

An indispensable aid to all astronomical observations of this kind is the photographic plate; since it is
common to observe such faint stars a long exposure
of the plate is often necessary to record spectral lines
which the human eye could not possibly see.

Since the Sun is by far the brightest object of our
skies we shall look at it first. It is so bright that it provides sufficient light to illuminate the Earth, the Moon
and all the other planets in the Solar System. The
surface temperature must reach about 6000°C, and
its centre 15,000,000°C. From our discussion of
molecules at high temperatures we can see that even
at the surface of the Sun most molecules will be
broken down into atoms.

Let us examine the structure of the Sun more close-ly. If we use a lens to cast an image of the Sun on to a piece of white paper, the edge of the Sun's disc looks definite and sharp. The area within this disc we have already named as the *photosphere*. However, the photosphere does not mark the limit of the Sun's at-mosphere; rising to over 5,000 miles above it is the *chromosphere,* which is also a region of high tempera-ture. Beyond the chromosphere comes the much more extensive *corona*. Except during a total eclipse, when the Moon hides the solar photosphere, the chromo-sphere and corona cannot be seen without the help of instruments based on the principle of the spectro-scope.

On the brilliant photosphere we may often see dark patches known as *sunspots*. Sunspots in reality are not at all small, and can be many thousands of miles wide. These dark patches are of particular interest because their appearance has a far ranging effect on the rest of the Solar System; for example, it has been sug-gested that in some way they affect our weather con-ditions here on Earth, though this connection is now regarded as dubious. Rising out of the photosphere can occasionally be seen huge clouds of incandescent gas reaching great heights into the chromosphere; these are known as *prominences*. *Surges* and *flares* are short lived prominences which shoot out from the Sun.

Since the Sun appears so large to us from our posi-tion on Earth it is possible to examine each of these different portions of the Sun individually by pointing an astronomical spectroscope at the area which in-terests us. Naturally, since the disc is the most obvious of the Sun's features it has received most attention from spectroscopists. Fraunhofer had catalogued 567 absorption lines, but this is only a tiny fraction of the numbers which have been identified today. There are over 3,000 lines due to iron alone, 1,000 of which have never been observed in a laboratory on Earth. Titanium and chromium show over 1,000. Over 40 per cent of all the lines which have been seen are still unidentified and are probably due to relatively small amounts of molecules rather than atoms. In recent years space research has come to the aid of spectroscopy. Spectrographs mounted in rockets have been launched to observe the Sun and have given some important spectra which could not have been obtained from observatories on Earth because of the interference of the Earth's atmosphere. We now know of the existence of 69 elements in the Sun—29 more than Rowland had managed to identify in 1897.

As might be expected, the areas of sunspots are cooler than the rest of the Sun's surface—4,000°C instead of 6,000°C—and so we might also anticipate that molecules, in addition to atoms, will be capable of existing there. The spectroscope shows this to be just the case and has given evidence of molecules such as titanium oxide in sunspots. In addition spectroscopy has shown that there is a remarkable flow of high temperature gas in and out of sunspots.

As we have seen, one of the most interesting portions of the Sun is the chromosphere. Nature very conveniently comes to the astronomer's aid in his observations of the chromosphere. At intervals the Moon passes between the Earth and the Sun, blocking out all light from the Sun's main disc. This is known as a total eclipse. Quite by chance it so happens that the Moon is situated at such a distance from us that, during a total eclipse when it covers up the main disc, it does not cover up the chromosphere. During the brief few seconds of a total eclipse astronomers are able to photograph the spectrum of the chromosphere. In such a case the spectrum consists of bright lines. Earlier we saw that the Fraunhofer lines, caused by absorption of light by the chromosphere, are dark. We should expect the bright lines of the chromosphere to correspond exactly with the dark lines. A close inspection of the two shows, however, that there are very slight differences. Because of these differences spectroscopists are able to explain some of the interesting physical and chemical reactions which are taking place in the chromosphere beyond the main body of the Sun.

Prominences, the huge clouds of gas which pour out above the chromosphere, are so bright that they can easily be seen by eye during total eclipses, and they are easy to photograph. Most impressive films have been taken showing their flames, hundreds of thousands of miles long, licking up and pouring down on to the Sun's surface. The spectrograph shows that large quantities of hydrogen and of metals are present in these flames; the pink colour which can be seen is due to single atoms of hydrogen. The corona, surges and flares can also be spectroscopically examined in the same way. The total result of the combined efforts of astronomers and spectroscopists is that the Sun is no longer quite the mysterious body it once was.

The Sun is 93,000,000 miles away, and one thing we can say with absolute certainty is that, even if space travellers could travel such immense distances, no man could ever "land" there: it is much too hot. Let us now look at things closer to home: our Moon, and the neighbouring planets. The Sun is so hot and so bright that we are able to see all the members of the Solar System by the light which it gives out. Since what we see of a planet here on Earth is due to the reflected light of the Sun, then that light will always be characteristic of the Sun. However, before reaching the Earth this light must pass twice through the planet's atmosphere; that is to say, once before and once after being bounced from the planet (Figure 9-1). Therefore, we can expect to see in the spectrum of the planet lines which are caused by the gases of the planet's atmosphere. (Of course, light must always pass through the Earth's atmosphere, too, and the astronomical spectroscopist must make allowances for this in his observations. It is for this reason that spectroscopes are sent up in rockets to make observations outside the Earth's atmosphere, where there is no risk of confusion due to the water vapour, carbon dioxide and other gases in our air.)

In these days of approaching space travel the atmospheres of other planets have become of great scientific interest. In the first place a space traveller would want to know what gases are surrounding him when he first sets foot on a strange world; after all, he

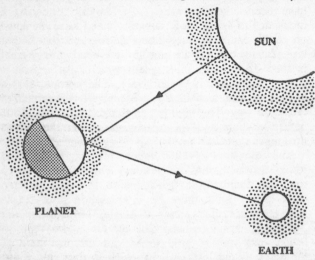

Fig. 9-1. Light passing through the atmospheres of the sun, a planet and the earth

might have the misfortune to have to breathe whatever vapours are surrounding him. A second matter of vital importance, and a subject which has stretched the imagination of man for hundreds of years, is what other form of life he is likely to encounter on a strange planet. If we expect to meet men on Mars who have two arms, two legs and one head, and perhaps blue eyes and fair hair, then we must expect the atmosphere on Mars to be similar to that on Earth so that a similar form of life to our own can be supported. And if we expect to find bacteria similar to most of the types we know on Earth, then there must be oxygen on the planet which will enable these living things to survive. The spectroscope can help us provide answers to these fascinating problems for it can give us a detailed picture of the gases which surround the planets.

The Moon is our nearest neighbour, being about a quarter of a million miles away from us; so far as we can tell it has no atmosphere. The fact that there is no water to be detected suggests that life as we know it could not exist there, and so any chance of our one day being able to meet Moon Men is very small indeed.

It was hoped that one problem, which for many years caused astronomers to argue amongst themselves, could be solved with the help of the spectroscope, and that is the problem of how the Moon's huge craters were formed. Were they caused by the surface of the Moon being struck by meteorites, or are they the craters of dead volcanoes? Craters of both of these kinds are known on Earth. In North America there are several large Moon-like craters caused by falling meteorites hitting the ground at terrific speeds; volcanic craters on Earth can also resemble those on the Moon. To try to solve the mystery spectroscopists attempted to identify any gases which might be escaping from the craters. It was hoped to be able to recognise the gas sulphur dioxide (which escapes from Vesuvius, one of the Earth's best known volcanoes). But all attempts to photograph the spectrum of any such lines failed until, on November 3 1958, the Russian astronomer Kozyrev identified gaseous carbon in an outbreak on the Moon's surface. Is the Moon so hot below its surface that it can vaporise carbon? This was a fascinating discovery which definitely suggested that the Moon is capable of producing volcanoes.

The planet Venus is our next nearest neighbour but astronomers are always faced with the difficulty that Venus is covered with thick cloud, which means that the surface of the planet can never be seen. However, spectroscopy does tell us that there are large quantities of carbon dioxide, some water, but no oxygen in its atmosphere. There still remains the interesting possibility that life can exist on Venus; however, our knowledge of Venus as a world is still very incomplete.

After the Moon and Venus our next nearest neighbour is Mars. Mars has a very thin atmosphere, similar to our own only in that the gas present in largest quantities is nitrogen. There are also tiny amounts of carbon dioxide and, probably, oxygen present. This encourages us to think that there might be some form of life on the planet. Ever since the astronomer Schiaparelli in 1877 thought that he could see through his telescope canals which might have been built by intelligent Martians, Mars has been the subject of both scientific speculation and fiction. Nowadays it is generally believed that there are no canals on Mars, nor even anything resembling them, and that Schiaparelli and others had been mistaken.

Perhaps the most famous of all science fiction novels is H. G. Wells's *The War of the Worlds*. Wells describes how Martians invade the Earth and for the first warning of the terror in store Wells calls on the spectroscope:

". . . Lavalle of Java set the wires of the astronomical exchange palpitating with the amazing intelligence of a huge outbreak of incandescent gas upon the planet . . . the spectroscope, to which he had once resorted, indicated a mass of flaming gas, chiefly hydrogen, moving with an enormous velocity towards this Earth."

All this seemed as unbelievable and fantastic sixty years ago, when it was written, as it does today. Yet, as other examples show, Wells's novels have touched on realism in a way which could scarcely have been foreseen half a century ago. The use of the spectroscope to detect life on Mars is a case in point, for in 1957 W. M. Sinton made the exciting discovery that the spectrum of Mars shows lines which might be due to molecules in plants or some other sort of vegetation. Bacteria also might well exist on Mars, so that the first space traveller to reach the planet should have some interesting findings to report back.

The spectroscope has helped astronomers solve mysteries in space much further afield than those in our own Solar System. Early astronomers had long been puzzled by faint patches of light in the sky which looked like clouds. Better telescopes showed these patches as though they were clusters of stars. Such a cluster became known as a *nebula* (meaning a little cloud); the nebula in Orion is a well known example of one of these. In 1864 Huggins pointed his spectroscope at a faint nebula in the constellation of Draco and, to his great astonishment, found that the spectrum of the nebula was not a complicated mixture of lines of different elements such as that produced by the Sun and other stars, but a single green line. Huggins believed that he had discovered a new element and, not surprisingly, he called it nebulium. However, in 1927 the green line was shown to be due to a form of oxygen, which we know to be a gas. A nebula of this kind, therefore, is not made up of solid matter but consists of immense clouds of glowing gas which have taken on wonderful shapes. On the other hand other nebulae, including the Great Spiral in Andromeda, were proved by the spectroscope to consist not of gas, but of stars. We now know that these "starry nebulae" are separate systems or galaxies, far beyond the galaxy in which we ourselves live.

For centuries philosophers have argued whether the space between stars is empty; the argument would probably still be going on today had it not been for the spectroscope. It was shown that light from certain stars was being absorbed on its long journey here to Earth, and that the atoms which were absorbing the light were hydrogen, sodium, calcium, iron and others. However, these atoms are present in space in only

the tiniest of quantities; it is only because stars are at
such vast distances from us, and the light from these
stars passes many atoms on its journey, that we can
detect the absorption. In the space of the Milky Way
there is about one atom of hydrogen per cubic centimetre; this is an incredibly rarefied amount when it is
remembered that a cubic centimetre of the air we
breathe contains 50 million, million, million atoms.

We see that Auguste Comte's assumption that man
would never be able to discover the composition of
the stars was a rash, though understandable, reckon-
ing. Every day the spectroscope gathers in more information to be pored over, studied and interpreted.
Luckily for the astronomer the powers of the spectroscope are not limited to giving him a knowledge of
the structure of the heavenly bodies; they also tell him
something about how they move in space, and at what
speeds. To understand how this new kind of information is collected we must once again examine waves
and their behaviour.

When a train, sounding its whistle, passes through a
station, a man standing on the platform hears the note,
or pitch, of the whistle change; the pitch increases
until the train is opposite the man and then decreases.
This, of course, is not due to the engine driver idly
experimenting with the controls of his whistle; a man
sitting in the train hears the whistle playing a steady
note. The same effect is produced by the whine of a
jet aeroplane engine or the hum of a motor car passing by; it is always heard when a moving source of
sound passes a stationary observer.

This effect is known as the Doppler effect and is
named after the man who first explained the phenomenon in 1842. Doppler's explanation is as follows. The
wavelength of a wave-motion, such as sound, is the distance between successive crests of waves; the frequency, or pitch, of the sound is the number of waves
passing a given point each second. Thus when you
hear middle C, 256 waves are entering your ear each

second. If the whistle of a train is middle C, then when the train is standing at the platform, this is the number of waves which enter the ear of a man on the platform. However, if the train moves rapidly towards the man, what is effectively happening is that more than 256 waves each second enter his ear, and the pitch of the note rises. The greater the velocity of the train, the greater is the change of pitch.

The Doppler effect occurs not only with sound but also with other wave-motions. In the same way, when a rapidly moving source of light is travelling towards an observer, more waves per second enter his eye than would from a stationary source. The result is that the light now has a higher frequency (shorter wavelength) and its colour moves nearer to the violet end of the spectrum than that of the stationary source. This is known as the *violet shift*. Conversely, a source of light moving away from an observer shows a *red shift*. So a spectroscope pointed at a sodium lamp fitted on an outward going spaceship should in theory show the D-lines as slightly more orange than the normal colour and to be shifted slightly towards the red end of the spectrum.

These effects are not nearly as easily observed as is the Doppler effect in sound. Only when the source of light is very rapidly moving indeed is any change of colour measurable; a star is such a source. But only a very sensitive instrument, such as a spectrograph, can detect these changes by recording how the lines in the spectrum are moved towards the red or the violet. It is by measuring these shifts of the Fraunhofer or other lines in a star's spectrum that an astronomer can calculate the speed of the star towards or away from the Earth.

Plate XII shows some of the classic spectra of distant galaxies photographed by the American astronomer M. Humason. The hazy central band in each red shift spectrogram is the spectrum of each galaxy. The two faint dark absorption lines due to calcium are to be seen at the end of the white horizontal arrow heads. The sharper upper and lower spectra in each photograph are merely spectra of laboratory substances taken for comparison so that the shifts of the calcium lines can be seen more clearly.

Spectra of five galaxies are shown in Plate XII; the distances of these clusters of galaxies from us are truly immense, and range from Virgo at 14,500,000 light-years to Hydra at 700,000,000 light-years. A *light-year* is a measure of distance; it is the distance which light is capable of travelling in one year; one light-year equals about 6,000,000,000,000 miles. The amazed realisation of astronomers, looking at photographs such as these, was that the further a galaxy is away from us, then the greater is the red shift of the spectral lines. In other words, the further a galaxy is from us, the faster it is moving away from us. Thus the spectroscope led astronomers to the remarkable discovery that *the universe is expanding*. We in our own galaxy are moving with the rest of the universe. Professor Fred Hoyle has likened our movement to that of a raisin in a pudding. As the pudding cooks it steadily swells. The raisins do not swell, but every raisin moves away from every other raisin. If you are able to imagine yourself sitting on such a raisin you would be able to see all the other raisins moving away from you.

The most distant galaxy to have its speed measured has been shown to be moving at 85,000 miles per second. There are still more distant galaxies which have been photographed but they give off too faint a light to enable their spectra to be measured.

It is in this way that the spectroscope gives us a wonderful general view of the behaviour of the components of the universe; but for things closer at hand it is capable of giving even more detailed information. We can imagine a planet to be like a ball in space. In our own Solar System the balls rotate in orbits around the Sun. At the same time as they rotate around the Sun, they spin on their own axes. The axis of the Earth lies between the north and the south poles. In each period of 24 hours the Earth spins once on its axis, and for that reason different parts of the Earth's surface face the Sun at different times and the 24 hour period is alternately split into night and day. It should be obvious, therefore, that the Earth's surface must spin through space at a great speed in order to complete its journey in 24 hours; moreover, a man standing near the equator must be moving through space at a greater speed than a man standing near the north pole. (We are never conscious of the great speed at which we are moving because our atmosphere moves along with us at the same speed.)

Other planets spin in space just as does the Earth; it is possible to measure how fast a planet is spinning by looking at distinctive features on the planet's surface, such as one of the white spots on Jupiter or a dark area on Mars, and noting the time taken by the feature to make a complete rotation. Some planets are found to have longer, and some shorter days than we have here on Earth.

As a planet spins, one portion of it moves towards us, and one portion moves away from us. In just the same way, if you hold a penny vertically on a table in front of you and cause it to spin by flicking the right hand edge, the right hand half of the penny will always move away from you and the left hand half towards you. Spectroscopists realised that they could make use of the Doppler effect to measure the rate of spin of a planet by pointing the spectroscope at opposite sides of the planet. The approaching side should show a violet-shift and the receding side a red-shift, and the amounts of shifts of the spectral lines should enable the rate of spin to be calculated.

The first object in the sky to have its spin measured in this way was not a planet, but the Sun. The observations of sunspots had told astronomers that the Sun turns once on its axis every 25 days, and by pointing a spectroscope at opposite edges of the Sun's disc it was possible to see the shifts of the Fraunhofer lines in the two cases. The rate of rotation of the Sun calculated by this method agreed very closely with that determined by observations of sunspots and once more showed astronomers how valuable an asset was the spectroscope.

The Doppler effect was used to confirm the speeds of rotation of some of the planets of the Solar System, and in doing so solved a number of other problems which had troubled astronomers. One of the most interesting objects to be seen through a telescope is the planet Saturn (Plate XIII). Saturn, like the other planets, is shaped like a slightly flattened ball, but unlike the others is surrounded by the famous rings, made up of numerous small bodies moving round Saturn in the manner of dwarf moons. Spectrographs were taken of one edge of the planet's disc, and also of the rings at the same side. The spectra of both the planet and the rings showed violet-shifts; in other words the planet and its rings rotate in the same direction. However, the rings nearer the planet showed a larger shift to the violet than did the outermost rings. This remarkable observation proved that the outer rings rotate at a slower rate than do the inner ones. James Clerk Maxwell, the physicist, had made a brilliant mathematical calculation which forecast this movement of Saturn's rings, but it was not until the perfection of the astronomical spectroscope that his theory could be shown to be correct.

Our own Solar System is itself only a relatively tiny part of a great galaxy, the Milky Way. The Milky Way is shaped like a discus, or like an enormous Saturn. At one time it was believed that the Sun was near the centre of this discus, but this is now known not to be the case. Just as Saturn is surrounded by a system of rotating rings, the Milky Way consists of systems of rotating stars, and the spectroscope has shown that stars nearer the centre of the Milky Way are rotating round the centre of the Galaxy at greater speeds than those nearer the edge of the discus.

Astronomical spectroscopy is merely a small section of the whole subject of spectroscopy, and the examples given in this chapter are no more than a few picturesque descriptions of the achievements in this field during the last sixty or seventy years. Awe-inspiring as the vastness of space seems to us, we are capable of seeing but a minute fraction, and of what we see we can understand only a little. But so long as astronomers are able to trap light which was given out hundreds of years ago by distant stars, the spectroscope will be at hand to help uncover the mysteries of the universe.

10

The Invisible Spectrum

In Chapter 5 we saw how different colours of the spectrum occupy different amounts of the wavelength scale. Green, for example, has a wavelength range from about 5,400 Å to 5,000 Å. The full range of colour which a person with normal eyesight can see stretches from red at 7,600 Å to violet at 3,800 Å.

However it is a remarkable fact that persons who have been in danger of losing their sight from a growth of cataract and have had the crystalline lenses of their eyes removed by a medical operation can see deeper violet colours down to a wavelength of 3,100 Å. In other words they have a visible spectrum 700 Å wider than a normal person. Obviously the crystalline lens of the eye absorbs a certain amount of violet colours. The spectrum therefore is wider than was at first thought. Is it possible that it is even wider still than this, and that our eyes can appreciate only a certain width of the spectrum? This is undoubtedly the case as a number of experiments performed since the beginning of the nineteenth century have shown.

It was Sir William Herschel who, in 1800, tried to discover what lies beyond the visible red end of the spectrum (see Plate XV). He blackened the bulb of a thermometer with soot from a candle and held it just beyond the red portion of the spectrum. As he had hoped, the temperature of the thermometer rose showing that rays of energy which were not visible to the human eye were falling on the blackened bulb. He then placed his thermometer in various parts of the spectrum: at the violet end the temperature was least and rose as he moved the thermometer towards the red. Beyond the red the temperature was greatest showing that the invisible rays had the strongest heating effect of the whole spectrum. This was a most important discovery and Young, who first investigated the phenomenon of interference and did so much to establish the wave theory, described Herschel's experiment as one of the greatest since the time of Newton.

These rays of energy are known as *infra-red* rays. and can be detected with wavelengths up to about 1,000,000 Å; this is a great deal longer than the visible red of 7,600 Å. It was shown that the position of the maximum heating effect of infra-red rays varied with the material of which the prism was made. This is because many transparent materials absorb infra-red radiation; an ordinary glass prism, for example, absorbs a lot of it, but a prism made of rock salt allows most of it to pass unabsorbed, and one made of sylvine enables radiation up to 230,000 Å to be detected.

Infra-red radiation has quite a number of uses in everyday life. Although an electric fire is obviously giving out energy in the form of red light which we can see, it is also giving out a great deal more energy which we cannot see. This energy is infra-red radiation and it is this which is for the most part heating the air in a room. Poultry farmers use infra-red lamps as a relatively cheap way of keeping their chickens warm in the winter months. We have seen that there are a number of transparent substances which absorb infra-red radiation but do not absorb visible light. Some

photographic plates are sensitive to visible light but not
to infra-red; conversely it is possible to manufacture
plates which are much more sensitive to infra-red
than to ordinary light. This fact is made use of in
infra-red photography. On misty or foggy days
the wet and dirty atmosphere absorbs light, but infra-
red rays pass through and give very effective and striking pictures.

These long infra-red rays with wavelengths of
0.0023 cm. are still relatively small compared with
sound and water waves and it was not too long before it was discovered that there were radiations of
wavelengths which were even longer than those of infra-
red rays. Nowadays everybody is familiar with these
kinds of waves and we put them to very good use
in communications and broadcasting. In fact it is very
difficult to imagine modern life without the use of
them. These are *wireless waves* and they were discovered by Hertz; they were once known as Hertzian
waves after their discoverer; they travel at the same
speed as light, 186,000 miles per second, and behave
in the same ways as all the other kinds of wave motions we have so far discussed. They can be reflected
and refracted and show both interference and diffraction. But by comparison with the wavelength of visible
light they are truly immense and wireless waves have
wavelengths between a few centimetres and 15,000
metres. So the longest wireless waves are forty thousand million times greater than the shortest visible
violet light. Radiation in the part of the spectrum between the infra-red and wireless waves has also been
discovered; this portion is known as the *far infra-red*.

If the spectrum stretches to such fantastic lengths
below the red of the visible then perhaps it stretches
in the other direction beyond the violet. It was only
shortly after Herschel had discovered infra-red radiation that Ritter, in 1801, placed some solid silver
chloride just outside the violet end of the spectrum of
the Sun. If freshly made silver chloride is kept in a

darkened room or in a dark bottle it remains white in colour; if light is allowed to fall on it, it turns dark due to the formation of silver metal. This principle is the one used to produce images on photographic plates. Ritter found that the silver chloride outside the Sun's violet portion of the spectrum was darkened even when he made sure that no light was being reflected from any other part of the spectrum. This experiment proved that there were radiations beyond the violet, and these were named ultra-violet rays.

These new rays were found to have some most interesting properties. When certain substances were placed in the path of the rays the substances glowed with a peculiar light. For example, in ultra-violet light crystals of calcium fluoride glow with a bright violet colour: uranium oxide gives a green glow. This effect is known as "fluorescence" and can often be seen when a white shirt which has been washed with a modern detergent is placed under an ultra-violet lamp. Some laundries mark clothes with a number printed in a fluorescent dye. Only when an ultra-violet light is shone on the cloth does the number become visible. Certain substances continue to glow for minutes or hours after the ultra-violet radiation has been removed—calcium sulphide for instance—and this effect is known as "phosphorescence". Visitors to the Scottish lochs, tropical seas and many other regions will have been fascinated by the peculiar glow of the water on dark nights. This is commonly called phosphorescence but is due to minute living organisms in the water. The organisms give out material which is slowly oxidised, and the chemical produces light. This emission of light should be more properly called "bioluminescence".

Ultra-violet rays have been measured with wavelengths as low as 1,000 Å. So again we see that the spectrum is extended considerably from the lowest visible violet wavelength of 3,800 Å. Ordinary glass is not transparent to wavelengths below 3,300 Å; a quartz prism on the other hand will allow ultra-violet rays down to 1,800 Å to pass and one made of fluorspar extends the range to 1,200 Å.

The Sun's radiation contains large amounts of ultra-violet rays and in order to live a healthy life we must have a share of them. Through them the human body forms its vitamin D, and miners who spend their working days below ground are often given doses of ultra-violet lamp treatment to maintain their health. A deficiency of vitamin D in the body sometimes causes rickets disease and the ultra-violet lamp has become useful as a treatment. Poultry farmers not only use infra-red lamps for the health of their chickens, but also make good use of ultra-violet radiation. It is found that hens lay better and that eggs produce healthier chickens after treatment.

There are rays of still shorter wavelength than ultra-violet: X-rays and gamma rays. X-rays may have wavelengths as short as 0.00000001 cm. and gamma rays a

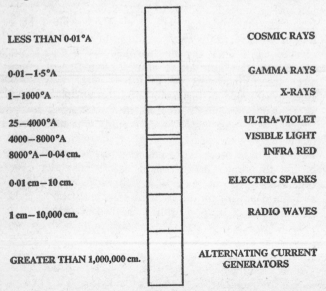

LESS THAN 0·01°A	COSMIC RAYS
0·01—1·5°A	GAMMA RAYS
1—1000°A	X-RAYS
25—4000°A	ULTRA-VIOLET
4000—8000°A	VISIBLE LIGHT
8000°A—0·04 cm.	INFRA RED
0·01 cm—10 cm.	ELECTRIC SPARKS
1 cm—10,000 cm.	RADIO WAVES
GREATER THAN 1,000,000 cm.	ALTERNATING CURRENT GENERATORS

Fig. 10-1. The electromagnetic spectrum

hundred times smaller than this. Rays with such tiny wavelengths have extreme powers of penetration of solid objects, hence the well-known use of X-rays in medicine to examine bone fractures in the body; gamma rays will penetrate such formidable obstructions as lumps of lead.

When Newton produced the first spectrum he was probably quite surprised to find that such a narrow beam of light could be spread into such a broad band of rainbow colours. Now that we have examined the spectrum more fully we see that what Newton was seeing was only a very tiny fraction of the spectrum's full range. The complete spectrum (it is called the electromagnetic spectrum) is shown in Figure 10-1. Its range covers wavelengths from ten thousand millionths of a centimetre to more than ten million centimetres. Of this huge expanse the visible portion occupies only a fraction of a millimetre; the remainder is invisible.

11

Using the
Invisible Spectrum

When James Watt made his first model steam engine there were many people who looked on the invention as nothing more than an amusing toy. It was not until he put his engine to work, driving wheels and performing little tasks, and eventually as a steam locomotive, pulling great loads on a railway, that it was realised that here was a discovery which would alter the face of nineteenth century England. Even the steam locomotive was only a modest beginning and soon the many applications of the simple engine were to revolutionise the industry of the world. Wollaston's first spectroscope was as plain and as amusing a toy as Watt's first steam engine; it was a convenient instrument which showed how light can be split up into rainbow colours. The work of Fraunhofer and Bunsen and the other nineteenth century spectroscopists showed to what amazing uses the spectroscope could be put. Their discoveries were as revolutionary to the progress of science as was the invention of the steam locomotive to the speed of travel and communication. And just as new applications were found for fresh designs of the steam engine, so were applications found for the invisible spectrum which were to widen man's under-standing of the nature of things around him in ways he could scarcely have hoped or dared to foresee.

Only shortly after their discovery, X-rays were put to use by doctors to diagnose bone fractures, and infra-red radiation soon found a use in long-distance photography. Spectroscopists saw that the properties of the rays of the invisible spectrum were similar in many ways to those of visible light; the question of most interest to them was whether all these radiations could be refracted. Sir William Herschel had shown that infra-red rays are refracted by a prism in exactly the same way as are light rays; Ritter had shown the same to be true for ultra-violet rays. Just as visible light of different wavelengths is refracted by different amounts, so infra-red and ultra-violet radiation of different wavelengths are refracted by different amounts. Soon it was found that the other invisible radiations could be refracted like light, but not necessarily by such a simple method as the use of a prism.

A light source such as a sodium flame was known to give characteristic yellow light and a spectrum showing a system of lines. Was it possible that the same source also gave out infra-red radiation and that the spectrum of the infra-red consisted of a system of lines? If so, here was a whole new field of unexplored information which could be just as rewarding as the visible spectrum. To settle the question it was necessary to build spectroscopes which could in some way detect these lines. Men of inventive minds set about the problem and the answer was all too clearly revealed: the whole of the electromagnetic spectrum could be made to show complicated series of lines and bands. With each new invention came a new branch of spectroscopy.

The rest of this chapter will be given over to brief descriptions of some of the new types of spectroscopes which were invented. The results of this work and the ways in which spectroscopists have extracted details and remarkable information from their new types of spectra have already been anticipated in Chapter 7. For example, a physicist can learn a good deal about the structures of atoms and molecules from the lines and bands of the visible spectrum, but the details of the infra-red, ultra-violet and X-ray spectra give him a vast new range of additional information. An infra-red spectroscope helps the oilman to control the amounts of certain fuels in petrol (which is a mixture of fuels); for the nuclear physicist it measures the amount of heavy water in a reactor; for Scotland Yard it helps the detective identify poisons. An ultra-violet spectroscope helps the doctor by estimating the vitamins in our diet, or the purity of penicillin. The X-ray spectroscope analyses metals and their structure as well as revealing how complicated substances like fibres are built up.

The principles which are used to interpret spectra of all kinds are very similar and at this stage little more need be said to illustrate the wonderful variety of uses of the spectra of the invisible radiations.

Appropriately enough the first man to make an *infra-red spectroscope* and to succeed in recording the lines of the spectrum was Sir John Herschel in 1840— forty years after his father, Sir William Herschel, had discovered the existence of infra-red radiation. At Cambridge he made a pact with two young friends that they would "do their best to leave the world wiser". Exactly how they proposed to do this they did not say, but John Herschel intended to make the legal profession his livelihood. However, undoubtedly inspired by his father and his aunt, Caroline Herschel, he had wider scientific interests. One of the men who was to divert him from his chosen profession of law to a study of science was Dr. Wollaston, and it was obviously the Doctor who encouraged his study of the spectrum with such happy results.

Herschel used a simple spectroscope to project the Sun's spectrum on to a thin piece of paper; the back of the paper he blackened with soot, and the front he

moistened with alcohol. The heating effect of the infra-
red rays caused the alcohol to evaporate and where the
paper dried, it became light in colour. However, the
paper did not dry evenly but left bands of moist surface. These bands of unevaporated alcohol showed
that, at certain wavelengths, infra-red radiation was
being absorbed by the chromosphere of the Sun and
was not heating the paper. Herschel had produced the
first infra-red absorption spectrum of the Sun.

Incidentally, this was not Herschel's only significant
contribution to spectroscopy. In 1839 he explained to
the Royal Society how he had independently invented
photographic sensitised paper and went on to carry
out experiments showing the action of the lines of the
solar spectrum on sensitised surfaces. As we have seen,
photographing spectra is one of the most important
methods by which a spectroscopist records his results.

Since an infra-red spectrum can be obtained with
such ease little need be done to adapt Wollaston's
spectroscope to its new task. Glass absorbs most of the
range of infra-red radiation and so we must not use it
in any parts of the infra-red spectroscope; both prism

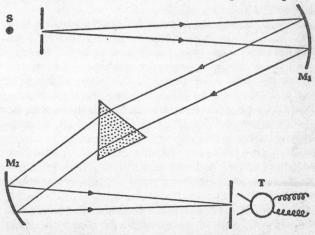

Fig. 11-1. Optical arrangement of an infra-red spectroscope

and lenses must be made of quartz or rock-salt, which allows the radiation to pass unhindered. Better still, we can abandon the use of lenses altogether and employ concave metal mirrors. Figure 11-1 shows the design of a suitable spectroscope. Light from the source S passes through the slit to a concave mirror M_1, thence to the prism and a second concave mirror M_2. The infra-red spectrum can be recorded on a special photographic plate, or another method is to use a thermopile, T. A thermopile is merely an instrument which records the heat energy falling on it by deflecting a galvanometer. By rotating the mirror M_1 a line of the spectrum can be made to fall on the thermopile, and the deflection of the galvanometer will be a maximum. By the continual adjustment of M_1 the whole of the infra-red spectrum can be mapped out.

Diffraction gratings may also be used in infra-red spectroscopy, and Rowland had a brilliant idea which not only avoided the use of a prism but also dispensed with lenses. He ruled the narrow lines of a grating on the surface of a concave mirror; in this way the radiation can be both diffracted and brought to a focus in a single operation.

The design of the *ultra-violet spectroscope* is also basically faithful to Wollaston's original design. Like the infra-red, ultra-violet radiation is absorbed by ordinary glass and so quartz or fluorspar prisms and lenses are used. The photographic plate is the most useful method of recording the spectrum and manufacturers have gone to considerable trouble to help the spectroscopist by designing plates which are particularly sensitive in this region of the spectrum.

Even though it was found possible to make very sensitive plates it was still found that part of the ultra-violet radiation was being "lost" inside the spectroscope. It was realised that there were two possible causes. First, a photographic plate consists of a reactive chemical surface spread evenly on a sheet of glass; holding the chemical surface to the glass and protecting it is a thin layer of transparent gelatine. Before any light can reach the reactive chemicals it must pass through the gelatine, which, like many other transparent substances, absorbs ultra-violet radiation. The only solution to this problem was to try to reduce the gelatine layer so that the radiation would have to pass through only a short thickness of absorbing material. The attempt was successful and, using plates with specially thin layers of gelatine, it is possible to photograph ultra-violet radiations at much shorter wavelengths than a normal plate would allow.

The second reason for the disappearance of some of the radiation was, surprisingly, the *air* in the spectroscope. Air behaves like gelatine and absorbs ultra-violet radiation. The only solution to this problem was to build vacuum-tight spectroscopes and to pump out all the air. Yet again the range of spectrum which could be examined in detail was extended and provided a new branch of spectroscopy: the *vacuum ultra-violet*.

X-rays, as we have seen, have wavelengths about 10,000 times smaller than visible light, and building a spectroscope to examine the rays presents special problems. Since the wavelengths are so short we cannot expect prisms or diffraction gratings to be of any help in forming a spectrum; it is possible to machine lines on a grating with 5,000 lines per cm.: to diffract X-rays we should need to draw 10,000 times this number of lines in each centimeter. In 1912 the German physicist Max von Laue suggested that the particles of a crystal of a substance which are arranged in a regular pattern might possibly be used as a natural diffraction grating for X-rays. A crystal of a simple salt such as sodium chloride has the shape of a cube and the particles which make up this cube are arranged in layers. If you imagine the shape of a large transparent modern office block to represent the crystal, then the particles could be pictured as footballs placed one at each corner of every room in the building to form the crystal: the rest of the block would be empty

space, without rafters, girders or walls. Looking at the
building from any side would show the layers of footballs, or particles, resembling the parallel lines of a
diffraction grating. It so happens that in a crystal of
sodium chloride the particles are separated from each
other by about 1A—which is roughly the separation
of lines which we should have to draw on a grating if
we hoped to diffract X-rays.

Sir William Bragg and his son set to work to construct a spectroscope using a thin crystal to diffract a
narrow beam of X-rays. As a grating the thin crystal
was entirely successful and the X-radiations, like visible light, could be made to give spectra, and could be
photographed and detected by other methods. The
most important result of the Braggs' work was that
they were able to show that the particles making up a
crystal of sodium chloride were actually *atoms* of
sodium and of chlorine situated about 1A from each
other.

These were the first experiments in *X-ray spectroscopy* which is now one of the most fruitful means
of determining the structures of, not only crystals, but
other solids as well as gases and liquids.

And so we see that spectroscopes have been built
to cope with radiation which is both a great deal
shorter and a great deal longer than the wavelength of
the visible spectrum. The band of rainbow colours was
just a starting point to push outwards, higher than the
violet, and lower than the red. But infra-red spectroscopy, ultra-violet spectroscopy and X-ray spectroscopy are themselves merely fresh starting points.
We have not yet mentioned *microwave spectroscopy*,
developed in World War II and dealing with radiation
of wavelengths from 1 mm. to 30 cm., nor *radio frequency spectroscopy* which can investigate waves many
kilometers long. Then there are off-shoots of spectroscopy in which somewhat different principles are involved but are nevertheless closely related to the subject. For example, in 1919 Aston invented the *mass-*

spectroscope which was capable of separating atoms of different masses into a spectrum and which has contributed greatly to our understanding of the physics and chemistry of isotopes.

The end is by no means in sight. Science is often compared to a clearing in the centre of a huge forest; the larger the number of trees you cut down, the bigger becomes the circumference of the clearing and the more trees there are for you to attack. The same is true of spectroscopy. Every day in one of the many thousands of laboratories in which a spectroscope is used a new and important discovery is made which may lead to the existence of a dozen other problems waiting to be solved. Science itself is an ever widening spectrum.

APPENDIX

Making a Spectroscope

Building your own spectroscope is not at all a difficult task, although the more refined and capable you require your instrument to be will determine how much effort you need put into the job. Most of the equipment necessary can be found in the home, and no more tools are required than those to be found in a tool-kit or small workshop. However, the most vital components of the spectroscope, the glass optics, must be bought. A suitable set of optics is:

Flint glass 60° prism
Object lens, 10 in. focal length
Condensing lens, 8 in. focal length
Collimator lens, 6 in. focal length
Eye-piece lens, 1 in. focal length.

A suitably sized prism would be one of side 2 in.; lenses of diameter about 1½ in. will be adequate (the values of the focal lengths suggested above are only the approximate requirements).

If you have no experience of handling spectroscopic or other optical equipment begin by making the simplest kind of spectroscope. In addition to your optics your main equipment will be six bottles, all of the

same size and fitted with flat corks of the type shown in
Figure 12-1. Corks of this kind are ideal for mounting
the lenses; cut a slit in the top of each of four corks so
as to hold each lens vertically and firmly. Strips of insulation tape used as shown in Figure 12-1 will add
even greater security.

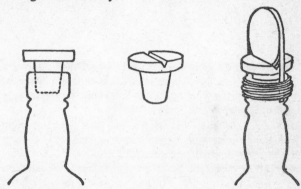

Fig. 12-1. A simple lens holder

With the fifth bottle make a table for the prism by
gluing or pinning a 6 in. × 6 in. piece of tin to the top
of the cork (Figure 12-2). The last bottle is used to
support a slit (Figure 12-3), which may be made
from a 6 in. × 12 in. piece of tin bent at right angles
as shown; in the centre of the vertical section cut a ½
in. diameter hole and across this fix with selotape two
razor blades to form a narrow vertical slit.

PRISM TABLE   **SLIT**

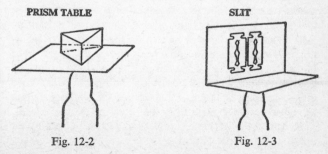

Fig. 12-2   Fig. 12-3

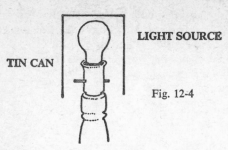

LIGHT SOURCE

TIN CAN

Fig. 12-4

As your first light source use an electric light: a reading lamp will do; cover the bulb with an inverted tin can in which you have cut a ¾ in. diameter hole (Figure 12-4).

Before arranging the parts of your spectroscope check the focal lengths of your lenses. This can be done quite simply by focusing the light from a distant window on to a sheet of white paper. Adjust the position of the lens so that the sharpest possible image of the window frame is cast on the paper. The distance between the paper and the centre of the lens gives you the required focal length.

Arrange the condensing lens between the source and the slit so that the light from the source is focused on the slit (Figure 12-5). Both the distance of the lens from the source and its distance from the slit should be equal to the focal length of the lens. Behind the slit place the collimating lens so that the two are separated by a distance equal to the focal length of the lens and so that parallel light is projected to the prism. Adjust the prism so that the light passing through it is bent as little as possible (this is known as the position of minimum deviation). You can check the path of the light by placing a piece of white card at various points of your optical set-up and observing the image. Make sure that light passes through the centre of all your lenses by appropriately adjusting the heights of the lenses. You can easily arrange this by moving the corks up or down in the bottle necks.

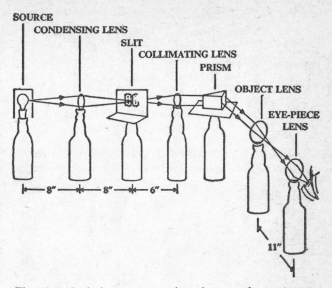

Fig. 12-5. Optical arrangement in a home-made spectroscope

Behind the prism place the object lens and collect the light from this in the eye-piece. The object lens and the eye-piece should be separated by a distance equal to the sum of their focal lengths. With this set-up in a darkened room and with your eye close to the eye-piece you should now be able to see a continuous spectrum. The best spectrum can only be found by trial and error, by carefully adjusting the width of the slit and the positions of the prism and lenses.

Once you have obtained a good spectrum you can replace your light bulb by a flame source and begin your emission and absorption experiments.

Of course this set-up is only a temporary affair and if you meet with success you might decide it worth while to build a more permanent spectroscope. Figure 12-6 shows the outline of a permanent instrument in which the prism, collimating and object lenses are fixed in one assembly which is bolted into a light-proof

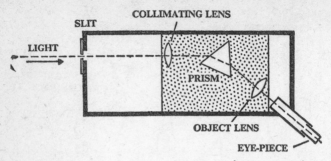

Fig. 12-6. A more permanent spectroscopic arrangement

box; to the box is attached an adjustable slit and a movable eye-piece. The success or failure of most experiments with a spectroscope depends a great deal on the careful lining up of all the optical parts. For this reason the prism and lenses must be in the best possible position which can be found to produce a good spectrum before permanently fixing them in the apparatus.

Books for
Further Reading

Light in Your Life by Irving Adler. Dobson, 80 Kensington Church Street, London, W.8.

Isaac Newton by Patrick Moore. A. and C. Black Ltd., 4-5 Soho Square, London, W.1.

Isaac Newton by E. N. da C. Andrade. Parrish & Co. Ltd., 55 Queen Anne Street, London, W.1.

Measuring the Universe by Henry Brinton. Methuen & Co. Ltd., 36 Essex Street, London, W.C.2.

Colours and How We See Them by H. Hartridge. Bell & Sons Ltd., York House, Portugal Street, London, W.C.2.

Tricks of Light and Colour by H. McKay. Oxford University Press, Amen House, Warwick Square, London, E.C.4.

A *Textbook on Light at an Introductory Level* by L. Mackinnon. Longmans, Green & Co. Ltd., 48 Grosvenor Street, London, W.1.

Galileo and Experimental Science by R. B. Marcus, Chatto and Windus Ltd., 40-42 William IV Street, London, W.C.2.

Light by B. M. Parker. Wheaton & Co. Ltd., 143 Fore Street, Exeter.

Guide to the Stars by Patrick Moore. Eyre & Spottiswoode Ltd., 22 Henrietta Street, London, W.C.2.

Light and Colour by Frederick Healey, and *The Meaning of Light* by C. A. Ronan, are both published by Weidenfeld & Nicolson (Educational) Ltd., 20 New Bond Street, London, W.1.

INDEX